Making Friends with the Stars

EVERYDAY HANDBOOKS

Making Friends

with the

STARS

by
Arthur J. Zadde

revised by
Theodore A. Smits
Brooklyn College Observatory

Barnes & Noble, Inc., New York
Publishers • Booksellers • Since 1873

This is an original Everyday Handbook (Number 227). It was written by distinguished authors, carefully edited, and produced in accordance with the highest standards of publishing. The text was set on the Linotype in Caledonia and Caslon Old Face by the Hamilton Printing Company (Rensselaer, N. Y.). The paper for this edition was manufactured by the S. D. Warren Company (Boston, Mass.) and supplied by the Canfield Paper Company (New York, N. Y.). This edition was printed by the General Offset Company (New York, N. Y.) and bound by the Sendor Bindery (New York, N. Y.). The cover was designed by John O'Neill.

About the Authors

The late Arthur J. Zadde was born in Russia and was a graduate of Moscow University, the Institute of Mining Engineers, and the Academy of Artillery. He came to the United States after the revolution in 1917 and worked in the Standard Oil Research Laboratories. Mr. Zadde was fascinated by the stars and planets; for many years he observed the sky and made maps of the constellations. His method of calendrical circles has received widespread acclaim among starwatchers and in 1949 his *Guide to the Heavens* was published.

Theodore A. Smits, who revised the original *Making Friends with the Stars* and brought it up-to-date, has been the Director of the Brooklyn College Observatory since 1951. He is also Associate Professor of Physics and Deputy Chairman of the department, and has conducted classes in astronomy, astronomical laboratory, and advanced work in independent study and research. Professor Smits has also taught at the University of Pennsylvania, Lehigh University, and the Polytechnic Institute of Brooklyn, and has done work with refractors at the Flower and the Cook observatories. A graduate of the City College of New York, Professor Smits studied at the University of Pennsylvania and received the M.A. from Columbia University.

Preface

THERE ARE SCORES of excellent books on the stars, but most of them are not for the general reader because they offer him too much. The average reader and would-be stargazer is more interested in the facts of astronomy than in the abstruse methods that enable the astronomer to penetrate the mysteries of the universe. Books that discuss at great length the advantages and drawbacks of reflectors and refractors, the relative merits of altazimuth and equatorial mountings, and the details of telescope optics frighten away the potential stargazer; they give him the impression that without the help of costly paraphernalia the sky and stars are beyond his reach.

On the other hand, there are too few books that facilitate for the beginner the problem of locating and identifying the stars and constellations. Professor Walter Bartky of the University of Chicago writes in the Preface to his distinguished book *Highlights of Astronomy*: [1] "The particular difficulty always encountered was the student's early discouragement when he could not locate for himself the stars and planets in the sky." It is the purpose of *Making Friends with the Stars* to overcome this difficulty.

[1] Chicago: University of Chicago Press, 1935. Reprinted in the "Phoenix Science Series," University of Chicago Press, 1961.

The primary reason for the discouragement so often felt is the inadequacy of existing starmaps. There is no end to starmaps and devices purporting to acquaint the beginner with the constellations, without a knowledge of which enjoying the sky is impossible, but they are so designed that they are of value only to those who *already* know the constellations. Some of them may serve their purpose, but generally they lack a definitive system that would make the identification of stars and constellations easy for the veriest beginner.

Such maps are particularly unsatisfactory to the city dweller, whose sky is never really dark. Often only the brighter stars are visible to him; consequently, the constellations appear defective. Their identification by the usual methods becomes a hopeless undertaking. As a matter of fact, the unfavorable conditions for the city dweller partly prompted the writing of this book.

The sky picture is ever changing, but the most frequently encountered starmaps are drawn only for certain hours (usually 9:00 P.M.) on certain dates (usually the first and sixteenth of each month), and the fledgling observer is directed to face the cardinal points of the sky, where he will see the looked-for celestial objects. For one thing, he may not know where the cardinal points—north, east, south, and west— are, particularly at night, when the sun is not there to guide him. There is no doubt that he may see the objects, but it is very doubtful that he will recognize them. He sees the sky and the stars with uneducated eyes.

There are other difficulties. The specified hours may not be at the disposal of the observer, or the sky may be cloudy, clearing up a few hours later, when the map is no longer of any use. Sometimes, tables are supplied showing which other map has to be substituted, and the observer may eventually orient himself. But this takes much more enthusiasm and patience than the average stargazer can muster, with the result that he becomes disappointed and discouraged.

Failures like these are made unthinkable by the unique

method proffered in this book. The starmaps are correlated to the sun's movement in the sky, and thus to our calendar and watch, so that they are usable *at any hour on any date.*

These maps repatriate, so to speak, our sun, putting it back in the sky among the other stars where it belongs and whence it is banned by all other starmaps. As a result, the starmaps are not mysteries, but are fully intelligible to the layman. He realizes at once the interdependence between a star's visibility and the sun's place in the sky.

To enjoy the fascinating hobby of stargazing, one has to be at home in the sky. This one can achieve only by knowing the constellations. But in order to identify a constellation, the beginner has to see it in its entirety. He can do this best without an optical instrument. A telescope's field of view is so small that it cannot encompass a constellation in full. Binoculars and field glasses are designed for seeing small objects or details invisible to the naked eye. If the reader is eager to widen his experience, he can do so by acquiring one of these rather expensive instruments plus a more advanced guidebook—but only after he has mastered the sky with his unaided eye.

This book is written for an observer who has no optical aid, and many a reader will be fully satisfied with its modest contents. He will have gained up-to-date notions about the stars and our solar system, and he will have become acquainted with a goodly number of stars and constellations. He will experience a kind of peculiar friendship for the stars, and every clear night, with every glance at the sky, he will recognize a few of his new friends. He will recognize them by their distinctive features, and their presence in or absence from the sky will no longer be shrouded in mystery but will exemplify a well-understood consequence of our tiny planet's journey in space. He will experience a unique, never-dimming satisfaction in knowing which of his celestial friends he can expect to see and which he must wait a specified time to see.

But for others this will be only the start. They will take

such a liking to stargazing that they will be tempted to delve into the more substantial literature about the heavenly bodies and our universe. For them astronomy will become an inexhaustible source of stimulation. The late Sir James Jeans, one of the foremost astronomers of our time, called astronomy the "most poetical" of the sciences; I would add "and the noblest."

—ARTHUR J. ZADDE

Reviser's Note

ONCE upon a time, and not so long ago either, some people thought of astronomy as a dull, static, and possibly exhausted subject. They felt that nothing much was changing, nothing really new was being discovered. But astronomers knew better. What a wealth of new instruments, techniques, and ideas have developed in just a few years! To mention a few: the Schmidt camera, radiotelescopes, inertial guidance systems, artificial satellites, photoelectric photometry and spectroscopy, and such concepts as a dynamic and evolving universe and cosmic curvature.

In this revised edition of Arthur J. Zadde's *Making Friends with the Stars*, much new material has been added to bring the book up to date, reference data have been calculated through 1970, and some of the topics mentioned above have been included to stimulate interest. The original flavor of the book has, I trust, been preserved. I am grateful to Professor Theodore G. Mehlin of Williams College for reading the manuscript and making helpful suggestions.

The Zadde method of presenting the stars, constellations, and planets in terms of "calendrical circles" is unique. Although the professional astronomer uses different co-ordinates, the scheme offered here has the great virtue of being simple, straightforward, and readily understood. It employs only the simplest arithmetic. It is assumed that the reader wishes to study the stars without optical aids of any sort, but he should not overlook opportunities to visit nearby observatories and planetaria.

If this book helps you to gain insight into a most fascinating subject and stimulates you to pursue its study further, I shall feel content. *Go out—look at the stars.*

—THEODORE A. SMITS

Table of Contents

1

Introducing the Stars

TO THE ancient and medieval worlds it would have seemed either sacrilegious or preposterous to dare compare our sun with a star, so overwhelmingly great appear the differences in size and brightness and in the parts they play in man's life. The sun, source of light and heat, thus of all life on earth, was worshiped as a deity, whereas the stars were thought of simply as lanterns hung up for the night by the gods.

As the body of scientific knowledge grew, the possibility that the sun might be a star gained credence. Eventually, the data accumulated by modern astronomers provided unshakable proof that the sun and the stars are of a kind. Before we proceed in our study of the night sky, therefore, let us review briefly what we know about this star to whose family the earth belongs.

THE SUN is a globe of gas some 864,000 miles in diameter —more than 100 times the diameter of the earth. Its weight is 332,000 times that of our planet. One circuit of the sky— or what seems to us to be a circuit of the sky—takes about 365 days to complete. The path of the sun as seen from the earth is called the **ecliptic.** Like the earth, the sun rotates on its axis. While the earth rotates once in 24 hours at all latitudes, however, the period of the sun's rotation varies from 25 days at its equator to 34 days near its poles. It is from this variation that we conclude that the sun cannot be a more-or-less solid body like the earth.

The sun is incredibly hot, as we think of hotness. At its surface the temperature reaches approximately 10,000° F. Atomic physicists, who view the sun as a large hydrogen–helium nuclear reactor, have estimated its interior temperature to be as high as 15,000,000° F. The energy developed by the sun is enormous; each square foot of the sun's surface emits energy at the rate of 8,000 horsepower. What is the source of such intense activity?

Recall Einstein's famous equation
$$E = mc^2,$$
where E is energy, m is the mass of the material converted into energy, and c is the speed of light. In the sun, as in most stars, hydrogen is the fuel supply. Four atoms of hydrogen are "burned" to form one atom of helium. Since four atoms of hydrogen are more massive than one atom of helium, a small amount of mass is left over. It is the conversion of this small portion of mass that produces such tremendous energy.

Since we know that the total output of energy created by this solar process is almost beyond imagining, it follows that an immense amount of mass must continually be changing into energy. The sun converts, in fact, 4 million tons of matter every second. One might well ask how the sun can withstand such a huge loss of substance. How much longer can it last? The answers lie in the great total mass of the sun, which has been radiating in substantially the same way for 3 or 4 billion years and will continue to radiate for at least that much longer. We need not be fearful that our sun is a spendthrift. It settled down to a state of mature conservatism long ago, leaving riotous living to such stars as Rigel (pronounced *Rī'jĕl*) and Betelegeuse (pronounced *Bee't'l jōōz*), whose remaining life expectancies are of the order of 8 million years.

The visible surface of the sun is called the **photosphere.**

Yerkes Observatory Photograph

THE SUN'S CORONA,
PHOTOGRAPHED DURING AN ECLIPSE

(To protect your eyes from severe injury, never look directly at the sun except through a heavily smoked piece of glass.) This surface is opaque, thus preventing us from seeing the sun's interior. Surrounding the photosphere are various layers of gases: the **chromosphere** (probably under ten thousand miles thick), the **inner corona** (a few tens of thousands of miles thick), and the **outer corona.** Photographic evidence indicates that the outer corona extends well over a million miles from the photosphere; radiotelescope evidence shows a cutoff of radio signals, presumably by the corona, some 5 million miles above the photosphere. It has been suggested that upper atmosphere effects on the earth may be caused by streamers from the corona, a distance of 93 million miles!

Sunspots are the familiar dark blemishes on the photosphere near the solar equator. A large sunspot can be seen to move across the face of the sun from left to right in about two weeks, thus demonstrating that the sun does rotate, and that, like the earth, it rotates from west to east. An average spot has an umbra (dark area) of 11,000 miles in diameter, and a penumbra (less dark area) of 23,000 miles.

Sunspots are associated with powerful magnetic effects both on the sun and on the earth, and evidenced by disturbances affecting telegraph lines and radio transmission. Sunspot activity apparently follows cycles of about 11 years, a cycle consisting of a period during which spots are scarce followed by a period during which they are abundant. In successive 11-year cycles the magnetic polarity of the spots is reversed, so therefore a complete period lasts about 22 years. It appears that there may be some connection between sunspot activity and events on the earth, but this matter must be studied much more thoroughly before any relation can confidently be asserted.

In absolute terms, the sun is rather above the average size for stars, at least in comparison with the stars of its immediate neighborhood. Its brightness, for us, of course, far exceeds that of any other heavenly body. The visual comparison of the sun with other stars raises the question of distance.

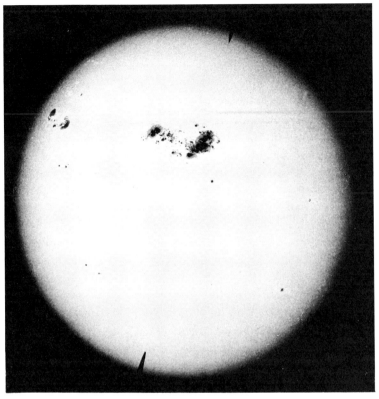

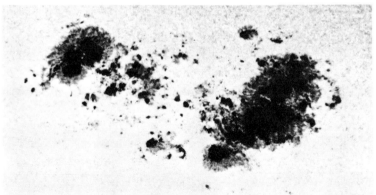

Photograph from the Mt. Wilson and Palomar Observatories

TOP: SPOTS ON THE SUN'S SURFACE
BOTTOM: THE GREAT SPOT GROUP OF APRIL, 1947

THE APPARENT BRIGHTNESS or faintness of a star, like that
of any other source of light, depends on its distance from the
viewer. As long as we do not know the distance of a star,
we obviously cannot estimate its real, or intrinsic, brightness,
although we can measure its apparent brilliance with great
accuracy. It was, therefore, an epoch-making event when,
in 1838, the German astronomer Friedrich Wilhelm Bessel
succeeded in determining the distance of a small star of the
constellation, Cygnus (pronounced *Sig'nus*), the Swan.

At present the distances of several thousands of stars are
known; and since the fact is also known that the brightness
of a source of light decreases as the square of its distance
(for example, when twice as far, light appears one-fourth as
bright; when three times as far, it seems one-ninth as bright),
we can calculate the intrinsic brightnesses of the stars and
then compare the stars with each other.

The apparently brightest star of the night sky is Sirius
(pronounced like "Serious"), the so-called Dog-Star, of the
constellation Canis Major, the Greater Dog. (Note that the
planets are not stars.) If Sirius were placed beside the sun,
it would be 23 times as bright as the sun. If the sun were
removed to the same distance as Sirius, our parent star would
be barely bright enough to be perceptible to the naked eye.
Sirius is not, however, instrinsically the most brilliant star.
In the Northern Hemisphere Rigel of the constellation Orion
(pronounced *Or ī'ŏn*) is 32,400 times brighter than our sun.[1]
Because Rigel is so much farther way from the earth than is
Sirius, it looks only one-fifth as bright as Sirius. Thus the
proximity as well as the size of Sirius determines its prominence in the night skies. As a matter of fact, Sirius is seventh
on the list of nearest stars, not counting the sun.

I said "not counting the sun," for the earth and sun are so
close to each other judged by astronomical distances that
they may be considered as being at virtually the same place.

[1] It is thought that a variable star (see p. 21) assigned the name S Dora-
dus, located in the southern celestial hemisphere, is at least 600,000 times as
bright as the sun.

They are, after all, only 93 million miles apart. Of course, 93 million miles is no trifle by ordinary human standards; an automobile averaging 60 miles per hour would need 175 years to cover the distance. The next nearest star, however, is 280,000 times that distance from us. Ninety-three million miles is indeed trivial in the abysses of the universe.

A star's apparent brightness depends on its distance, and so also does its apparent size; but the stars' distances are so enormous that all stars except our sun appear to be points of light even through the most powerful telescopes.

This statement requires explanation, for besides the earth there are quite a few heavenly bodies belonging to our solar system, i.e., under our sun's gravitational control, which appear to us also as stars. They are not real stars or suns, however, but dark, cold bodies. They look like real stars because of the sunlight falling on them and reflected to us. A few of them even outshine real stars—with light borrowed from the sun. These spurious stars consist of the planets, their moons or satellites, and the asteroids. These bodies are quite near us compared with real stars; with the exception of the remote planet Pluto, they appear through a telescope not as points but as small disks. This difference in appearance between the planets and the stars, by the way, enabled the great astronomer William Herschel to discover the planet Uranus in 1781. Uranus is so faint to the naked eye that it had eluded earlier detection, whereas the other planets then known had been familiar from earliest times.

Because the distance and volumes cited by astronomers when talking about the solar system are notoriously difficult to remember, I shall describe an imaginary model to illustrate them—a device I happened to run across when I was a boy, and which I have never forgotten because of the familiar things used in the comparison. But before doing so I must amplify a little what has already been said about the solar system. For the present we shall consider only the planets and the moon, ignoring the asteroids, comets, and meteors.

There are nine planets. In the order of their distances from the sun they are Mercury, Venus, Earth, Mars, Jupiter, Saturn, Uranus, Neptune, and Pluto. The largest of them is Jupiter; its diameter is well over ten times that of the earth. The smallest planet, Mercury, has only one-twentieth of the earth's volume. The mass of all the planets combined is less than one-seventh of 1 per cent of that of the sun. Keep these relationships in mind as we proceed to our model.

IMAGINE OUR SUN reduced to the size of a large pumpkin, a good 2 feet in diameter. The earth would then be the size of a small pea and 250 feet (an average city block) away from the pumpkin, and our moon would be 6 inches away from the pea and the size of a large poppy seed. Jupiter, the largest planet, would be located 1,000 feet farther away and would be about the size of an apple. The most remote planet, Pluto, would be 35 blocks away from the Jupiter-apple; it would be a second small pea. All the other planets are omitted lest the picture become too complicated, but their sizes would be intermediate between the apple (Jupiter) and the large poppy seed (our moon).

To make the picture still more realistic for those who know New York City, imagine the pumpkin (the sun) near the Public Library at the intersection of Fifth Avenue and 42nd Street. The pea (the earth) would then be at the intersection of Fifth Avenue and 43rd Street; the apple (Jupiter) would be at the corner of 47th Street; and, finally, another small pea (Pluto) would be located at the Metropolitan Museum of Art, Fifth Avenue and 82nd Street. Thus, for 40 city blocks all we have is a large pumpkin and nine small balls from pea- to apple-size; between them—nothing but an empty void. "Miserably unpeopled," as Addison would say. And the nearest star [2] after the sun is (on our scale) 10,000

---

[2] Alpha Centauri (pronounced Sĕn to'rē) belongs to the constellation Centaurus of the southern celestial hemisphere. Actually, Alpha Centauri's companion star, Proxima ("nearest"), is closer, but it is invisible to the naked eye. Except in southernmost Texas and Florida, Alpha Centauri is invisible in the United States.

miles (200,000 city blocks) away! By coincidence this near-est other sun is of about the same size and brightness as our sun, so that in our picture it, too, would be a good-sized pumpkin.

Pause for a moment and consider these distances. We have a pumpkin and nine small peas and apples distributed over 40 city blocks; then we encounter nothing, nothing, and nothing for 10,000 miles (more than three times the dis-tance from New York to San Francisco), when we find only another pumpkin, surrounded, perhaps, by its apples and peas. The emptiness of the universe is unimaginable.

LET US RETURN to Sirius, the brightest star in the sky and also one of the nearest to our sun. Judging from its color, the surface temperature of Sirius would be higher than that of the sun, since any source of light becomes whiter with an increase in its temperature. For example, if we heat a block of iron it stays dark up to nearly 1,000° F. At 1,300° F. it becomes dull red, at 1,650° F. cherry red, at 2,000° F. orange, at 2,150° F. yellow, at 2,550° F. white, and at 2,800° F. daz-zling white. Indeed, Sirius is intrinsically 23 times brighter than and nearly twice as hot at the surface as our sun. Sirius is said to be a white star, whereas the sun is a yellow star. And there are stars hotter than Sirius! What the limit of a star's surface temperature is we do not know, but estimates as high as 200,000° F. have been suggested.

Sirius is five times larger than our sun in volume, yet its mass is only two and one-half times as great. This is not par-ticularly remarkable. Sirius enters into another comparison, however, which is quite extraordinary.

Revolving about Sirius is a diminutive companion star known as Sirius B (Sirius itself being Sirius A). Sirius's volume is 200,000 times that of its dwarf companion; if Sirius were a very large pumpkin, its companion would be a very small pea. Do you suppose it would require 200,000 such tiny companions to make up the weight of Sirius? Nothing of the kind; only three!

Sirius B must necessarily be incredibly dense, so dense that 1 cubic inch of its substance would weigh almost a ton. How such tremendous density could originate is a matter of speculation. Atoms, you will remember, are the minute particles of which all matter is composed—particles that less than a century ago were believed to be indivisible. They have since been found to be elaborate structures made up primarily of protons, electrons, and neutrons so related that the atom is considered to be chiefly empty space. There are reasons to believe that at the temperatures prevailing at a star's center the atoms partly collapse, and that in a star like Sirius B the atomic structure is completely shattered. The protons, electrons, and neutrons are thus packed into a relatively small space. This process accounts for the great densities of such stars.

Sirius B and stars like it are known as **white dwarfs.** Scores of such dwarfs have been discovered. Like Sirius, Procyon (pronounced *Prō'si-on*) of the constellation Canis Minor, the Lesser Dog, has a dwarf companion. One cubic inch of Procyon B weighs 200 tons!

In contrast to the dwarf stars with their unbelievably great densities are the very low density **red giants.** The gases that make up the red giants are more rarefied than any man-made vacuum. An example of this class of stars is the famous Betelgeuse of the constellation Orion—famous because until recently it was believed to be the largest star. Its diameter is about 300 times that of the sun, but it is so rarefied that its mass is only 15 times as great.

Betelgeuse pulsates, swelling and shrinking in volume. Because of the resulting variation in brightness it is called a **variable star.** It was, incidentally, the first star the diameter of which was measured directly. This was accomplished in 1920 by means of an optical device called an interferometer (pronounced *interfēr ómeter*). Before the invention of the interferometer, astronomers had to determine the diameter of stars by indirect methods.

Here it must be said that in respect to volume, density, and brightness some stars may surpass others a million and even a billion times, but that the *mass* of the overwhelming majority of stars is between ten times and one-tenth the mass of the sun. Betelgeuse, therefore, is also a rather exceptional star as to mass. Other stars of great mass are Rigel, which we have already met (see p. 6), and Antares (pronounced *An-tar'eez*) of the constellation Scorpio, the Scorpion; each has about 40 times the mass of our sun.

Several stars are known to surpass Betelgeuse in volume. The four largest of them are the just-mentioned Antares, a star of the southern celestial hemisphere invisible in our latitudes, Ras Algethi of the constellation Hercules, and a star of the constellation Auriga (pronounced *Ôrï'ga*), the Charioteer. Antares is 50 per cent larger in diameter than Betelgeuse, but the star in Auriga is estimated to be nine to ten times as large.

This last star, by the way, is invisible not only to the naked eye but even through the most powerful telescope because it emits infrared light, invisible to the eye. It can be photographed, however, by means of a camera equipped with special plates.

Many stars surpass our sun in intrinsic brightness, but of the 50 stars nearest us only four are of greater instrinsic brightness. Three of them we have already met: Alpha Centauri, Sirius, and Procyon. The fourth is Altair (pronounced *Al-tah'ear*) of the constellation Aquila (pronounced *Ak'will-a*), the Eagle. The remaining 46 stars are telescopic, i.e., invisible to the naked eye.

Omitting the details, we can say that the great majority of these 50 nearest stars are inferior to the sun in volume, temperature, and mass; the sun seems to be an above-average rather than an inferior star, as was believed not so long ago, when it was compared only with the brightest stars in the sky.

So FAR we have been talking about distances mostly in

vague, relative terms. True, the sun's distance from the earth has already been given as 93 million miles, but such huge figures are virtually meaningless because we cannot visualize them. For instance, the nearest star, Alpha Centauri, is 25 trillion miles away, and Rigel 3 quadrillion miles; but can you visualize these distances? Certainly not. In order at least to avoid such cumbersome figures the astronomers invented a new unit, the **light-year,** which is the distance that light travels in one year. Light travels 186,000 miles in one second, so a light-year is somewhat less than 6 trillion miles. The distances of Alpha Centauri and Rigel become 4.3 and 540 light-years, respectively. The sun's distance from the earth expressed in light-years is only 0.000016 light-year, or 8.3 "light-minutes."

Less than two centuries ago it was believed that light reaches any point in the universe instantaneously. In 1676 the Danish astronomer Olaus Roemer, observing the orbits of Jupiter's satellites, came to the conclusion that even light requires time to travel. But so firmly rooted was the belief in the instantaneous propagation of light that over half a century elapsed before Roemer's theory was universally endorsed.

The nearest star, Alpha Centauri, is 4.3 light-years away. The great telescopes of the world, however, penetrate far deeper than this into the abysses of space. The giant 200-inch Palomar telescope of the California Institute of Technology has photographed groups of stars possibly as far as 6 billion light-years away!

Note that the most remote celestial objects have not been observed but photographed, for in this respect photography is superior to telescopy. This is due to the fact that the photographic plate fixes a star's image by means of a time exposure. The effect of the star's light on the human eye is not similarly cumulative. Special photographic plates reveal stars that otherwise would elude the eye, even if supplemented by the most powerful telescope. These stars make absolutely no im-

hotograph from the Mt. Wilson and Palomar Observatories

EXTERIOR OF THE DOME OF THE 200-INCH HALE TELESCOPE
AT PALOMAR MOUNTAIN

pression on the eye because they shine by infrared light. A star of the constellation Auriga, at present supposed to be the largest of the giant stars (see p. 11), is an example. Furthermore, modern radiotelescopes can explore the longer electromagnetic radiations emitted by planets, stars, and "outer space."

To return to stars we can see, the apparent brightness of a star is called its **apparent magnitude.** In ancient times the stars were grouped according to their apparent brightnesses into six classes, from first to sixth magnitudes, the brightest stars being those of the first magnitude. When scientific methods for the determination of brightness were introduced, it turned out that a star of sixth apparent magnitude was one-hundredth as bright as an average first-magnitude star. There are a few stars that are brighter than first-magnitude stars; these stars have negative magnitudes.

TABLE 1

Star	Apparent Magnitude	Absolute Magnitude	Luminosity
Sun	—26.7	4.8	1.0
Alpha Centauri	0.3	4.7	1.1
Procyon	0.37	2.7	7.4
Sirius	—1.42	1.45	23.5
Betelgeuse	0.78	—5.6	15,500
Antares	0.98	—3.9	2240
Rigel	0.15	—6.4	32,400
Sirius B	8.3	11.2	0.003

A star's intrinsic brightness (discounting distance) is called its **absolute magnitude.** Of course, both types of magnitude are only abstract notions; besides, each step on the scales of magnitude represents a factor of 2.512 (either brighter or fainter), which is extremely impracticable to work with, especially in cases of fractional magnitudes. Therefore, a new scale of brightness has been devised, in which the sun serves as the unit, and the absolute brightness of a star, when compared with that of our sun, becomes its luminosity. The abstractness of magnitudes and the merits of luminosity are best illustrated by the table on page 14, compiled for the stars we have already discussed.

Even on exceptionally clear nights the naked eye perceives only stars of the first six magnitudes; fainter stars make no impression on the retina. How can this observational difficulty be remedied?

WHEN A WAVE OF WATER strikes the openings of a one-inch and a ten-inch pipe, more water will enter the ten-inch pipe. The same sort of thing takes place when a light wave coming from a star strikes the eye and a telescope. In both cases all light which has entered is collected at one point, the focus; but whereas the aperture of our eye lens, the pupil, is only about one-fifth of an inch in diameter, the diameter of the mirror of the telescope on Palomar Mountain is 200 inches; hence, the diameter of its aperture is 1,000 times the diameter of the pupil of the eye. The light-gathering power of a telescope depends upon the area of its lens or mirror, and this area is proportional to the square of the diameter. Hence the Palomar telescope gathers $1,000 \times 1,000$, or 1 million times as much light as does the eye. This is also the ratio of the light conveyed to the focal plane of the telescope to the light conveyed to the retina of the eye.

The visual telescope will always be indispensable, but it is losing more and more ground to the telescopic camera, first, because the photographic plate is more sensitive than the eye, and second and more important, because the observations by the camera are fixed on a plate and can be filed away for further use. Besides, photographic observations are free of any possible error or prejudice on the part of the observer. As a matter of fact, beginning in 1887, the work of photographing the entire sky has been carried on systematically; it is now divided among observatories in different parts of the globe. We can now compare plates showing the same part of the sky made more than 50 years apart and notice what changes, if any, have taken place.

Photograph from the Mt. Wilson and Palomar Observatories

INTERIOR VIEW OF THE HALE TELESCOPE
SHOWING THE REFLECTING SURFACE
OF THE 200-INCH MIRROR

16

The farthest planet, Pluto, was discovered by means of photographic plates. On the basis of mathematical calculations, Percival Lowell had predicted that an additional planet would be discovered, and astronomers, knowing that planets change their positions in the sky whereas stars, for all practical purposes, do not, conceived a plan to photograph at certain intervals that part of the sky where the presumed planet was thought to be. By comparing plates taken several days apart, a young astronomer, Clyde W. Tombaugh of the Lowell Observatory at Flagstaff, Arizona, spotted the new planet in 1930.

It is interesting to compare the discovery of Pluto with the discoveries of Uranus and Neptune.

Uranus was found by William Herschel in 1781 while he was scanning the sky. This heavenly body appeared in Herschel's homemade telescope as a small disk instead of as a point, as true stars do. It had been observed for nearly a hundred years, but observers had thought that it was a star.

The precalculated detection of Neptune is perhaps the greatest triumph of theoretical astronomy. After the discovery of Uranus by Herschel, its orbit was duly established. Later it was found that for some unknown reason the planet deviated from its proper course. Finally, in 1845, a French astronomer, Urbain J. J. Leverrier, concluded that the gravitational attraction of an unknown heavenly body might be the cause of Uranus's eccentricity. It took Leverrier about a year to finish his calculations, but because he lacked up-to-date charts (photography was not yet known, and reliable charts were only in the making) he could not actually locate the new planet. In 1846 he wrote to the German astronomer Johann Galle in Berlin, asking him to scan the sky in a certain region. Galle possessed new charts, just completed in Germany. It is told that he interrupted his own birthday celebration upon receipt of Leverrier's letter and went at once to the observatory, where he located the long-sought planet in less than an hour, very close to the place which

Leverrier had indicated. Leverrier was a theorist exclusively, and after learning of Galle's success never took the trouble to have a look for himself at his brain child.

John Couch Adams, at that time a student at Cambridge, England, had conceived the same idea independently. After four years of calculations he finished his work in 1845, nearly a year ahead of Leverrier. He forwarded his calculations to the Astronomer Royal at Greenwich, but nothing was done until 1846, when the results of Leverrier's work became known and proved to be almost identical with Adams's solution. Even then, work with the Cambridge University telescope was hampered by the lack of charts. Report of the Berlin discovery reached Cambridge before the planet was found by the local observatory.

The importance of the camera attached to the telescope cannot be exaggerated. The most delicate measurements can be made on photographic plates. In general, much of the contemporary astronomer's work is mechanized; do not imagine that Tombaugh, while hunting for the hypothetical Pluto, was comparing the photographic plates point for point. Since many thousands of stars, as many as a hundred thousand, can be seen on one plate, such work would require months or years. Instead, Tombaugh used a most ingenious apparatus called a blink microscope, or, better, a blink comparator. Two plates covering the same part of the sky and taken a certain time apart are placed side by side and viewed intermittently, one plate at a time. If both plates are absolutely identical, the observer gets the impression of seeing one and the same plate; but if the plates differ, the changes are at once shown by blinks at the points of difference. Tombaugh's work was, nevertheless, extremely painstaking, as not the whole of a plate but only a small part of it can be scanned at one time.

In addition to the visible radiation that we call light, the stars, nebulae, and galaxies emit radio waves. These waves, ranging from about an inch to 100 feet in length, are detected by huge antennae connected to sensitive electronic receivers. Many of these antennae take the shape of large parabolic dishes; others are in the form of wire-mesh arrangements stretched along the ground for perhaps a quarter of a mile, and are called arrays. Such large instruments, if made of solid sheets of metal, would be both heavy and unwieldy (they have to be turned like any optical telescope to study some particular portion of the sky), and they would be subject to severe wind and storm hazards. Fortunately, wire-mesh construction has proven to be quite effective.

It has been found that hydrogen gas, which pervades interstellar space, emits characteristic radio waves approximately 21 centimeters (about 8¼ inches) long. This radiation is capable of penetrating dust clouds (unlike visible light) and thus opens a new window into space. With radiotelescopes we have explored hitherto unknown "arms" of our galaxy and now have a clearer picture of its structure. The largest radiotelescopes now planned will enable us to receive signals from the very edge of the universe.

Several thousand celestial radio sources are now known, some of the most intense being located in regions where no star can be detected by optical telescopes.

MAN HAS BEEN TRYING to extend and refine his senses ever since that period of remotest antiquity when his curiosity was first aroused by the workings of nature. His unceasing quest for the truth about the universe has resulted in the invention of a remarkable series of instruments that have enabled astronomers to see farther, detect smaller differences among similar things, and otherwise bring more of the universe into their ken. But the astronomer with his instruments had always been essentially earthbound—until 1961, when Major Yuri Gagarin became the first voyager into space.

Orbital and suborbital flights since 1961 have given scientists valuable data about space and about the ways "spacemen" will have to adapt to extraterrestrial conditions. These flights have, however, been but preludes to the first genuine penetration of space, the manned flight to the moon.

By 1970, and perhaps as early as 1967, the United States

hopes to put three men into orbit around the moon and land two of them on the lunar surface. This immense technological effort, Project Apollo, will cost 20 billion dollars and involve 100,000 people. The necessary skills for Project Apollo will be developed by two-man teams orbiting the earth for as long as two weeks. Thereafter men will not have to depend upon the use of instruments such as telescopes to obtain detailed information about the moon. The riddles of the lunar surface will be solved by men walking upon it. And exploration of the moon will accomplish more than providing additional knowledge about a small, cold satellite: new light will be shed on the origins of the solar system and on the nature of our galaxy and the entire universe.

We have become acquainted with stars similar to our sun: Alpha Centauri, Sirius, and Procyon; with giant stars like Betelgeuse and Antares, which are very tenuous; with dwarf stars like the companions of Sirius and Procyon, which are the densest stars; and with Rigel, a real giant as to mass (not volume) and luminosity. A new class of stars must be added to our list, namely, the **double stars.**

We must first distinguish genuine doubles from spurious ones. A genuine double is two stars, one of which revolves about the other, or both of which revolve about a common center. The periods of the circuits of double stars vary from a few days to centuries. A spurious double is made up of two stars that may be enormously far apart and without any connection whatsoever, but that are in the same line, or almost so, as seen from the earth. The genuine doubles are called **physical doubles, binary stars,** or **binary systems;** the others are called **optical doubles.** Many thousands of physical doubles have already been identified, and many more are expected to be found in the future. Incidentally, we have already met two binary stars, Sirius and Procyon. Generally speaking, the unaided eye cannot resolve such doubles, though a keen eye might detect a "double-double," Epsilon Lyrae. A few of the optical doubles are visible to the naked eye—for example, the stars Mizar and Alcor in the Big Dipper.

There is another interesting class of stars, the **variables** (see p. 10). The majority of these stars vary in brightness in regular periods, but quite a few of them do so irregularly. The lengths of these periods vary from a few hours to years. This class of stars is subdivided into several categories. Most of the variable stars are giants and far away; the precise mechanism of their variability is still unknown. The first to be discovered (about 1600) and therefore the most famous of the variables is the star Mira ("the wonderful"; pronounced *My'ra*) of the constellation Cetus (pronounced *See'tus*), the Whale or Sea Monster. At its maximum, Mira is of third magnitude; at its minimum, about ninth magnitude. This represents a change in brightness of about 100 times. The fluctuations in brightness are very irregular, and the cycle is completed in about 11 months. It is notable that quite recently Mira was found to be a binary star.

A **genuine variable** is a single star that changes in brightness periodically, but another type of variable, called an **eclipsing variable,** is simply a physical double so located that the plane of the common orbit lies edgewise, or almost so, to the line of our sight. One member of such a couple is brighter than the other and is periodically partly or totally eclipsed by the fainter star. One of the most famous examples of this class is the star, or rather the binary, Algol, of the constellation Perseus (pronounced *Pur'soos*). Algol is about three times the diameter of our sun; its fainter companion is somewhat larger. The fainter star partially eclipses the brighter one for about ten hours, after which Algol's original brilliance is re-established. The bright phase of the cycle lasts for sixty hours, so that the total period is about three days. This regularity has been maintained since the discovery of Algol's variations over two and one-half centuries ago. Well over 3,000 eclipsing binaries are known. Their periods of revolution run from five hours to twenty-seven years. The most commonly encountered period is two to three days.

The last and most mysterious class of stars is that of **novae,** or new stars. These stars are not really newcomers but existing stars that, for reasons unknown, suddenly increase enormously in brightness, then fade away after a period. The most spectacular nova was Tycho's Star, discovered by the Danish astronomer Tycho Brahe in 1572. It became so brilliant that it could be seen in midday. This nova was a star in the constellation Cassiopeia (pronounced *Kas-si-o-pee' ya*), but unfortunately it is not known which one. So far, about a hundred novae have been recorded. Most of them are recent discoveries which we owe to photography.

In 1937 a **supernova** appeared whose maximum luminosity was estimated at that of 350 million suns! Its surface temperature, however, was estimated at about 100,000° F., which is no more than that of some of the hotter ordinary stars. The novae and supernovae appear to be the results of explosions of stupendous magnitude—explosions which have so far defied completely satisfactory explanation, though nuclear physicists have offered partial explanation.

AFTER THESE general descriptions of the nature of stars, the question "What are they doing?" arises. To the eye stars seem motionless, fixed permanently in the same place, whence the common designation "fixed stars." The appearance of immobility is, of course, an optical illusion; these stars do move, but their relative movements, as seen from the earth, are so imperceptibly small that only after a substantial lapse of time can they be noticed, and even then only with the aid of the most delicate measurements. Such measurements were indeed made over a century ago, but only with great difficulty, since photography was not available.

The explanation of the apparent immobility of a star lies in its great distance. One of the nearest stars, Sirius, travels some 300 million miles in a year. But if we were to imagine Sirius to be a monster pumpkin, 4 feet in diameter, it would be located 20,000 miles from the pea representing our earth, and it would have moved in one year not quite three city blocks! Obviously, we could not notice a displacement equal to three blocks from a distance of 20,000 miles, but the astronomers' instruments can do that and better. Here again, photography is an indispensable help to science. Small as these displacements are, they can be measured on plates showing the same parts of the sky taken at different, preferably widely different, times.

But not all stars show such displacements; everything depends on the distance of the star and on whether the star moves across our line of sight or, although approaching or receding, remains on our line of sight. In the latter case the star could rightly be called "fixed," because on the photographic plate it would always occupy the same place. The astronomer uses another device to detect line-of-sight motion, namely, the spectroscope. Consequently, he can discover the speed and direction of any star.

By means of observations made over centuries and highly painstaking and ingenious computations, it has been quite firmly established that our sun with its family of planets is moving in the direction of the constellation Lyra (pronounced *Lī'ra*), the Lyre, with a velocity of 12 miles per second, and that it came, millions of years ago, from the region now occupied by the constellation Orion. The stars of these and all other constellations are also in perpetual motion, racing at various speeds in all directions. The motions of several thousand of the nearest and brightest stars have been determined, and analysis has led to the conclusion that our solar system and most visible stars move, like an enormous swarm of bees, within a certain area called the **Milky Way galaxy.**

The Milky Way galaxy is an aggregation of billions of stars, in the general shape of a thin disk that thickens at its center. Since the end of World War II this picture has been somewhat revised, so that today we envision our galaxy as a giant, rather loosely wound spiral. The arms of the spiral were detected by radiotelescopes, which came into their own only after 1945. The estimated diameter of the outermost spiral arm is 100,000 light-years. The sun and solar system are situated about midway between the center and the perimeter of the galaxy.

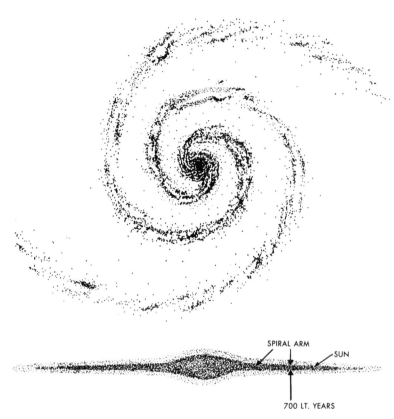

FIG. 1.—SCHEMATIC SKETCH OF THE MILKY WAY GALAXY

ABOVE: Face-on   BELOW: Edge-on

If we on earth look toward the flat sides of our galaxy, we see beyond the stars to the vast reaches of the universe, forming the dark background of the sky. This is possible because the layer of stars in this direction is not overly thick. If, however, we look toward an edge of the galaxy, the dark background beyond the stars disappears, the dense layer of stars in this direction quite obstructing our view. Instead, we see that faint belt in the sky called the **Milky Way.** This belt is necessarily faint, because it is produced by the light of numerous but very distant stars. The distance from our sun to the farther edge of the galaxy is about 80,000 light-years; to the nearer edge, about 20,000 light-years.

The Milky Way is often blotted out by unfavorable atmospheric conditions or moonlight. For the city dweller it is virtually never observable because of the glare of city lights.

The naked eye sees, of course, only an infinitesimally small number of the stars of our Milky Way galaxy, and even the most powerful telescopes only partly resolve it into individual stars. The distribution of the stars in our galaxy is not uniform; they are many **star clusters,** and luminous and dark clouds or **nebulae.** The dark clouds were formerly thought to be empty places in the universe, but at present they are considered to be huge masses of cosmic dust which obscure the stars behind them.

The spiral-shaped swarm of billions of stars forming our Milky Way galaxy revolves around a center that is believed to be in the direction of the constellation Sagittarius (pronounced *Saj-i-ta' ri-us*), the Archer. Contrary to what normally happens when a disk rotates, the stars move faster the nearer they are to the center.[3] In this swarm of stars our sun has a velocity of about 200 miles per second, completing one circuit around the gravitational center in about 200 million years, or one **cosmic year.**

Outside the boundaries of the Milky Way galaxy are billions of what appear to be nebulae or luminous clouds of gases in the sky. Not very long ago they were believed to be similar to the gas clouds in our own galaxy. We now know that they are in fact other stellar systems like our Milky Way galaxy. In order to distinguish them from the nebulae in our

---

[3] This situation is similar to that in our solar system: Mercury moves with a greater velocity around the sun than does Pluto.

galaxy, we call them either **extragalactic nebulae** or simply, and more appropriately, **external galaxies.**

One of the nearest of these external galaxies is the so-called Great Nebula in Andromeda (pronounced *An-drom'e-da*). The Great Nebula is the remotest object in the universe the unaided observer can see. Under particularly favorable conditions it appears as a small, hazy patch of light, for which reason in earlier days it was thought to be a nebula. It is 1.5 to 2 million light-years away and in size roughly compares with the Milky Way galaxy (see pp. 88–90). The remotest external galaxies so far detected are about 2 billion light-years away.

The external galaxies are by no means stationary; on the contrary, their velocities are even greater than those of the stars in our Milky Way galaxy. The behavior of these galaxies is most mysterious. We observe from their spectra that all galaxies save certain of the closest ones seem to be moving away from us with a velocity that is directly proportional to the distance of the galaxy from us. For example, if the first of two galaxies is twice as far away from us as the second, the first will be moving away twice as fast as the second.

Calculations based on various models of the universe give it a radius of 4 to 6 billion light-years. These calculations are founded upon assumptions that cannot as yet be conclusively proved, so it is possible that our notion of the age of the cosmos may have to be revised. This and many other similar questions have yet to be thrashed out by the astronomers.

2

Mapping the Sky

ALTHOUGH there are trillions of stars, only about 5,000 of them are visible to the naked eye, and even this many only under exceptionally favorable conditions. Since we can see only half of the sky at a time, the number of stars visible at one time is reduced to 2,500. Of these 2,500 stars, many are invisible because they are near the horizon, where the hazy atmosphere blots them out. So when we talk of "numberless" stars, we are very much exaggerating if we mean stars visible to the naked eye, or **lucid stars.**

If we roughly arrange the lucid stars into classes of integer magnitudes, we shall find that there are some twenty stars of first magnitude, fewer than a hundred of second magnitude, fewer than three hundred of third magnitude, and fewer than five hundred of fourth magnitude—a total of fewer than a thousand. The remaining stars, of fifth and sixth magnitudes will probably not be seen if the observer is bothered by moonlight, haze, or city lights.

Although the lucid stars are not numberless, there are, nevertheless, enough of them to confuse us. We can compare the evening sky to a map on which the cities are represented by dots without names; the larger the city, the larger the dot standing for it. Such a map will probably not be very helpful. But if the boundaries of the states can be drawn into the map and we are familiar with these boundaries, we shall be able to identify the cities more easily. If we wish to locate Jackson, Mississippi, on a map of the United States, we first try to locate the state of Mississippi. Once oriented, we can easily identify Jackson by its relative position and the size of its dot.

Similarly, the stars in the sky have been divided into groups called constellations. These groups are quite arbitrary, with imaginary outlines. The fact that these outlines, of course, are not visible makes the problem more difficult. However, the groups are so peculiar or individual that the eye develops skill in recognizing a particular constellation at a glance.

There is an extensive literature concerning the origin and history of the constellations' designations and the myths connected with them. In all probability many, if not most, of the well-known constellations were conjured up by the nomadic peoples who lived in ancient Chaldea (now Iraq) about 3,000 B.C. The Greeks wove their own myths and legends about the Chaldean constellations. Absurd as these myths may seem nowadays, they have a certain charm and help to familiarize us with the constellations they refer to.

As to the names of the individual stars, the reader may be surprised to find so many in Arabic. The reason for this is that during the Dark Ages (broadly speaking, the sixth to fifteenth centuries) only the Arabs continued to record observations of the sky, and their terminology has persisted.

At present, 88 constellations are recognized by astronomers, about a score of them belonging to the southern celestial hemisphere and invisible from the United States. Of the remaining constellations we shall ignore those that are not fully visible to the unaided eye.

We must make a distinction between the boundaries of a constellation and its contour or outline. The boundaries of the constellations were decided upon by the International Astronomical Union, whereas their outlines or contours are roughly determined by connecting their more prominent stars. For example, on Chart II (following p. 00) the stars forming the outline of the constellation Leo, the Lion, are connected by continuous lines and the boundaries of the constellation are dotted.

EVERYBODY KNOWS that the earth rotates on its axis once every 24 hours. All around the earth are stars, stars, and stars —among them, of course, our sun. During one **rotation** of the earth, i.e., within 24 hours, all the stars exposed to view in our latitudes pass us by. But besides rotating on its own axis the earth revolves around the sun, completing one **revolution** in a year, so that after six months it comes to a point in its orbit exactly opposite its former position. At that point, for an observer at the equator, the sun blots out all the stars

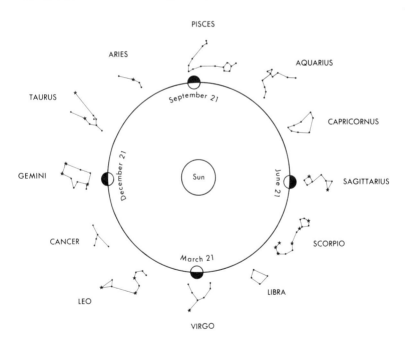

FIG. 2.—THE SEASONS AND THE ZODIACAL CONSTELLATIONS

that were visible at night six months earlier, and all the stars we could not see six months before become visible. For an observer at the north pole, some stars are visible the year round.

Figure 2 (p. 29), showing the twelve "zodiacal" constellations (see p. 63) which the earth passes during its yearly revolution, illustrates the foregoing remarks. At night the observer is in the black half of the circles representing the earth; during the day, in the white half. When in the white half, he cannot see any other stars but the sun; but when in the black half, he sees different constellations depending on where the earth is located in its journey around the sun. On the evening of March 21, for instance, he sees the so-called spring constellations Leo, Virgo, and Libra; during the day he could see, but for the sun, Aquarius, Pisces, and Aries, the autumn constellations. Six months later, on September 21, the picture is reversed: he sees Aquarius, Pisces, and Aries at night, but cannot see the spring constellations Leo, Virgo, and Libra during the day.

At the same evening hours, then, you cannot expect to see the so-called winter constellations in the summer, and vice versa. Every season has, for the same evening hours, its own constellations. There are, however, a few constellations that, in our latitudes, can be seen every night of the year. There are others that are visible almost every night, and so on. (We shall consider these matters in detail in Chapters 3 and 4.)

IF WE EXTEND the earth's axis of rotation, it hits, or nearly hits, Polaris, our North Star. Polaris appears virtually motionless because it lies on this extended axis. All other stars seem to us to describe circles around this star; the farther the star is from Polaris, the greater is the circle. At the earth's north pole, Polaris is almost at the **zenith,** i.e., directly overhead, so that for an observer at the pole the earth's axis of rotation is perpendicular to the horizon; here Polaris coincides with his **zenith point.** As he moves south, his zenith point, always plumb for the observer, moves with him, and Polaris and the zenith becomes separated; the farther south he travels, the greater the separation becomes. On the equator, finally, the separation between Polaris and the zenith is equal to a right angle: Polaris lies on the horizon, motionless, and all the other stars seem to circle around it.

The United States is nearly halfway between the north pole and the equator. Polaris's place in the sky is therefore nearly halfway between the horizon and the zenith. The movement of the stars around Polaris is counterclockwise if you face Polaris and clockwise if you turn your back to it. Some stars describe circles that are not large enough to take them below the horizon, so that they are always above the horizon and visible as long as the sun does not interfere. Most stars, however, rise sooner or later in the east and, after remaining various lengths of time in the sky, disappear again beneath the western horizon. Note that certain stars around the south celestial pole never rise for observers in the United States.

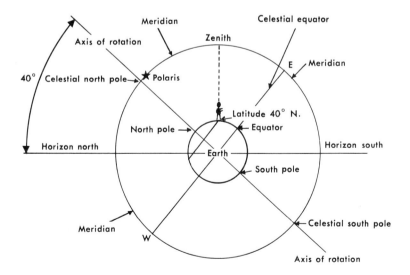

FIG. 3.—THE CELESTIAL SPHERE

Figure 3 shows the zenith for an observer at latitude

40° N., plus the other guidelines that are indispensable for orienting oneself in the night sky. The fortieth parallel, our reference in the chapters that follow, extends in the United States from New York City through New Jersey, Pennsylvania, Ohio, Indiana, Illinois, Missouri, Colorado, Utah, Nevada, and north-central California.

If we could see the entire sky, it would appear to us as a globe or sphere seen from within. For this reason we refer to the whole sky as the **celestial sphere.** We can, of course, see only one-half of the sky at a time, so we shall in succeeding chapters be speaking in terms of the **celestial hemisphere.** At the center of the celestial sphere floats our tiny earth, so small that it can be considered a point, i.e., as having no dimensions at all. The extended axis of rotation of the earth pierces the celestial sphere at two points (see Fig. 3), the **celestial north pole** near the star Polaris (pronounced *Poe-lay'ris*), and the **celestial south pole**.

An imaginary plane passing through the zenith of a place and both poles of the celestial sphere (as well as both poles of the terrestrial globe) leaves on the celestial sphere an imaginary circular line of intersection called the **meridian** of that place. The observer in Figure 3 points to the meridian and, simultaneously, to the point due south; if he should turn around, he would still face the meridian, but toward the north.

Surprisingly few people know the points due north and south of them. We need only remember that every day the sun crosses the meridian at noon [1] (usually not quite exactly, but closely enough for our purposes). If we face the sun then, we are at the same time facing the meridian and due south. To the left will be east, and to the right, west.

The meridian, or simply south–north, will be our basic line of orientation; therefore, we have to secure guiding points or marks that will enable us to know south and north

---

[1] Hence "meridian" from the Latin *meridianus,* meaning "pertaining to noon."

from our point of observation not only during the day but at night. Since every day at noon the sun is due south (see also Note A, p. 44), any object, the farther away the better, in line with the sun and us and discernible in the dark is a possible guidepost. As no great accuracy is required, if we go to a new point of observation that is not too far from the old, the old guidepost will continue to serve adequately. We need only a rough orientation, since the number of constellations is limited and their outlines are very characteristic and extended.[2]

It is most important to observe a safety measure already mentioned: when using the noonday sun for determining the meridian, you must protect your eyes with a well smoked piece of glass or with *very* dark sunglasses. Several layers of much overexposed film negatives will also do.

We now have our bearings in the night sky, taken from the sun. Our adventure is about to begin.

---

[2] A compass may be helpful for purposes of orientation, but it must be remembered that *magnetic* north is not the same direction as *astronomical,* or *true,* north.

3

The Charts and How to Use Them

THE SKY appears to us as a hemisphere seen from within. It is quite impossible to reproduce the entire surface of this hemisphere on flat paper. This is what the majority of starmaps try to do, with the result that the sky picture is distorted to such an extent that the constellations are recognizable only to those who are already familiar with them. A *small* part of the celestial hemisphere, however, can be represented with sufficient accuracy.

The area of Chart I (following p. 144) coincides with the top of the celestial sphere, around its north pole. It represents only 18 per cent of the celestial hemisphere and is, therefore, quite satisfactory. Chart II, showing the celestial sphere's equatorial zone (including parts of both celestial hemispheres) unrolled on flat paper, takes in 77 per cent of the celestial sphere. Given areas on Chart II are sufficiently accurate *while they are on or not very far from the meridian.* Every portion of the sky will be on the meridian once every day (the stars being visible only at night, of course) because the sky completes one apparent revolution around us every 24 hours. The upper halves of the charts are identical with the lower halves, but are drawn without guidelines in order more nearly to resemble what you will actually see.

The constellations included on Chart I are called **circum-polar constellations.** Like all other constellations, they complete a full revolution around the celestial north pole every 24 hours. They lie near enough to the pole almost always to be above the northern horizon. Since our horizon is always more-or-less obstructed and hazy, some of them will be difficult to see when they are close to the horizon. Nevertheless, the circumpolar constellations can be called **year-round** or **diurnal constellations.**

The constellations on Chart II are called **equatorial constellations.** The farther beneath the celestial equator they are, the fewer hours they remain above the horizon. In addition, they are "seasonal," as was explained on p. 30. Some of them are visible the greater part of the year (sooner or later in the evening); some are visible for only a few months.

When describing the constellations (Chapters 4 and 5), we shall begin with those of Chart I because they are diurnal, after which we shall continue with the seasonal constellations of Chart II. In order to assist the reader better to understand the charts themselves, however, we shall at this time present the following explanation of Chart II.

ON CHART II the sky is divided into 12 equal sections, conforming to the months in our year, by lines bearing the Arabic numerals 1 to 12. These lines do not change their imaginary places in the sky. We shall call them **calendrical circles—** *circles* because they are portions of great circles of the celestial sphere, and *calendrical* because they are so chosen that circle (line) 1 is on our meridian at *noon* on January 1, circle 2 at noon on February 1, and so on.

This division of the sky, in itself, is of no direct interest to the stargazer, since at noon the stars are invisible, but it enables us to determine at what hours of the day any section of the sky will be on our meridian. Beneath every circle is a timetable showing these hours for the first of every month. By this simple arrangement our calendar and watch are pinned to the sky. This particular feature is unique to these charts.

As an example, suppose it is 8:00 P.M., February 1. Examining the February 1 horizontal row of our timetables, we find 8:00 P.M. under circle 6. Looking south we do not see any very conspicuous stars near the horizon, but higher up and a little to the left we see the constellation Orion; still higher, the bright star Aldebaran (pronounced *Al-deb'a-ran*) with the Hyades (pronounced *Hī'-a-deez*), and to the right the Pleiades (pronounced *Plee'a-deez*); and finally, at and beyond the zenith, the constellations Auriga and Perseus.

Examining the hours of the timetables for one and the same day (say July 1), we notice that each circle, moving from right to left, crosses the meridian two hours later than its predecessor. This is so because each of the 12 circles crosses our meridian once every 24 hours. Since the starting point of our circles' timetables is noon, January 1, and all our intervals are two hours, all hours below the circles are even hours.

Every circle mentally drawn midway between two of these circles will cross our meridian at an odd hour on the first of the month. These imaginary circles are indicated only by corresponding numerals (decimal fractions), but they, too, have their timetables beneath.

Thus, for every full hour of the first of a month we know the circle (12 are drawn, 12 only indicated) that is on our meridian. Other times of the day can be rounded off to the nearer full hour without interfering with the locations of the constellations. This is explained in Note B, p. 45.

But how about the days of the month other than the first?

The corresponding circles can be determined rather accurately, as explained in Note C on p. 45, and such accuracy is required for locating single stars, but for locating constellations we can get along very well with the timetables of Chart II as follows:

Chart II 37

For the *first* week of a month we use the circle of the
first day of that month for the hour in question.
For the *last* week of a month we use the circle for
the *same hour* of the first day of the *next* month.
For all other days we use the circle between.

For example, for 8:00 P.M., Feburary 1 to 7, we use circle
6; for February 22 to 28, we use circle 7 (properly that of
8:00 P.M., March 1); for any other day in February we use
imaginary circle 6.5.

Suppose it is 10:40 P.M. on November 19. What part of the
sky will be on or close to our meridian?

We first round off our time to 11:00 P.M. Then we consult
the November 1 row of our timetables, finding 11:00 P.M.
under circle 4.5. As we are neither in the first week of November (which would require circle 4.5) nor in the last week
(which would require circle 5.5), we use circle 5. Facing our
meridian (south), then, we see very high in the sky, at the
zenith, the constellation Perseus with its star Algol and the
stars Almach (pronounced *Al′mak*), and Mirach (pronounced *Mī′rak*) of Andromeda; somewhat lower, the constellations Triangulum (pronounced *Trī-ang′u-lum*) and
Aries (pronounced *A′ri-eez*) with Hamal (pronounced
Ham′el); and still lower, the star Mira.

The same problem is solved in Note C on p. 45 by a more
accurate method with practically the same result, circle 5.1.

LET US REVIEW what each of the lines on Chart II represents. When the chart becomes perfectly familiar, its quick
and accurate use will become second nature. First, we remember that it shows the entire sky from the horizon to a
little beyond the zenith as we see it when facing south for the
space of all 12 months. The horizon-line on the chart is
straight, but to correspond with reality it would have to be
a huge circle—the circle of intersection of the celestial sphere
with a plane tangent to the earth's surface at our place of ob-

servation. Only when this circle is unrolled on our flat paper does it become a straight line.

A vertical line through our place of observation pierces the sky at the zenith. The zenith is always exactly overhead, but as the earth rotates on its axis (see Fig. 3, p. 31) the stars passing through the zenith point on the celestial sphere trace an imaginary circle. This circle, unrolled on our flat paper, becomes the straight zenith-line.

The celestial equator, shown by another straight line on the chart, is actually a huge imaginary circle running from exactly east to exactly west, intersecting the southern meridian a little higher than midway between horizon and zenith at latitude 40° N.

On the chart we encompass the entire sky at a glance, and the celestial equator seems to be level with our eyes, but actually it is rather high in the sky. In order to see stars and constellations higher than the equator (Lyra, Cygnus, Andromeda, Perseus, Auriga, etc.) we must bend our heads backward. The right way to use the chart, therefore, is to hold it above the head or almost so. If one of the stars of a constellation lies near the celestial equator, that fact will be emphasized in our discussion of the constellation in order to assist the reader in tracing the celestial equator.

The dashed curve on Chart II is the ecliptic, the sun's apparent annual path among (more correctly, in front of) the stars. Besides showing the sun's place in the sky for every day (see Note C, p. 45), the ecliptic is very useful in locating the planets, as they are never far from it.

If we see a bright "star" in the sky that is not shown on Chart II, we can be sure that the stranger is a planet. The Planetfinder (see pp. 124–132) will be our guide in identifying the planets.

ON CHART II the circles can be shown without great distortion as running parallel to each other. Actually, however, they are not parallel, but run from the southern horizon to the celestial north pole, upon which they converge. The celestial north pole is the center of Chart I. The lines or radii of Chart I are nothing but the ends of the circles of Chart II, and the celestial north pole is the center of their diurnal rotation.

In the sky the north pole almost coincides with the star Polaris. When we face due north, Polaris is the not particularly bright star (of second magnitude) on the northern meridian a little lower than midway between the horizon and the zenith. Polaris is almost motionless, being practically the center of rotation of the entire sky.

When facing due north, we have to use Chart I; conversely, when we wish to use Chart I, we must face due north. Facing north, we have to distinguish the upper meridian (from the zenith to Polaris) from the lower meridian (from Polaris down to the horizon). The timetables of Chart I refer to the *upper* meridian, from the zenith to Polaris; the lower meridian is crossed by the stars and constellations 12 hours later (see Note D, p. 48).

On Chart II the circles move clockwise, from east to west (see Note E, p. 48); on Chart I they move counterclockwise, yet they still move from east to west because we have turned around to face north. The circles of Chart I are, of course, used in the same way as the circles of Chart II, the only difference being that the "next" circle is to the right instead of to the left.

Suppose, for example, that it is 7:15 P.M., December 10. Rounding off our time to 7:00 P.M. and consulting our timetable for December 1, we find this hour under circle 3.5. As we are neither in the first week of December (when we would use this circle) nor in the last week (when we would us the circle for the same hour, 7:00 P.M., of the next month, January, i.e., circle 4.5) we have to use the circle between 3.5 and 4.5, circle 4. If we face the upper northern meridian (due north), then, we squarely encounter the constellation Cassiopeia.

The equatorial constellations (Chart II) are recognizable to the beginner only when they are on or not far from the meridian, because only then do they really conform to their patterns on Chart II (see Note E, p. 48), but the circumpolar constellations are always almost exactly as they are represented on Chart I, when the latter is properly oriented in accordance with the timetables. This is the case because Chart I comprehends a small area and only year-round constellations.

The circumpolar constellations are all conspicuous, with the possible exceptions of Cepheus (pronounced *See'fi-us*) and the Dragon's Tail in Draco (pronounced *Drā'co*), and there should be no difficulty in identifying them.

Charts I and II represent the visible part of the northern celestial hemisphere as it appears to the naked eye on an average cloudless and moonless night. On unusually clear and dark nights more stars may be visible, but when atmospheric conditions are poor or the moon interferes, fewer stars will be discernible, and portions of many constellations will be invisible. This may render the constellations unrecognizable for the beginner. Variations in visibility must always be borne in mind.

On our charts the names of the constellations are in capital letters. The charts are drawn for localities of latitude 40° N. but are fully satisfactory for the entire United States of America. Time, wherever mentioned, is standard time. If daylight saving time is in effect, *subtract* one hour from the clock time to determine standard time.

Practical Hints

It would be wrong to mislead readers into assuming that this subject is very simple; disentangling the maze of the sky is not easy. It requires enthusiasm and perseverance, and one cannot learn to recognize all of the stars and planets in a single evening.

On the first night, or nights, none of the starmaps is of great help to the beginner, because they are all utterly unrealistic. The sky is immense whereas our charts are necessarily extremely small. The constellations in the sky will appear huge in comparison with their tiny likenesses on our charts. It is equally impossible to represent accurately the comparative brightnesses of the stars by dots of various sizes. The beginner will be lost in the labyrinth of the sky until he becomes proficient in translating a star's magnitude on the map into its actual brilliance in the sky. Furthermore, the magnitudes of the stars on all starmaps are only approximate (see Note F, p. 49). Do not be disturbed if your first nights are not outstanding successes; it is only natural. The important thing is never to miss an opportunity to observe the sky, particularly on the rare nights when neither moon nor cloud hampers your vision.

Before going into the open, the novice must engrave in his mind the outlines of the constellation he is looking for, so that he will be quite familiar with its configuration. This is absolutely necessary for star identification, just as we cannot identify a person unless we know his lineaments.

At first, always start by establishing the location of the circle for your date and hour. After you have found your bearings proceed step by step to the neighboring constellations that have already **culminated,** or reached their highest points in the sky. This procedure refers mainly to Chart II (see Note E, p. 48).

Sometimes it is advantageous to scan the sky early in the evening, before the end of twilight, when the brightest stars first become visible. With the aid of our charts these stars can be identified and afterwards will serve as beacons.

Use **averted vision.** When you are looking for a faint object (for example, the Beehive in Cancer or the Great Nebula in Andromeda) that you know must be there but that you cannot see, do not look directly at the region you know it to occupy, but scan its immediate neighborhood. Often you will eventually perceive the faint object, though not sharply. The superiority of averted vision is due to the fact that the most sensitive area of the eye, the so-called yellow spot, is not located at the center of the retina. Also, when reading the charts at night, use a weak flashlight rather than a strong one, for the latter might blind you for quite some time. Still better, wrap the head of the flashlight in red tissue paper.

Observing a constellation near the zenith (such as Hercules, Cygnus, Perseus, or Andromeda) is difficult because it is uncomfortable. We instinctively turn around in preference to craning our necks, now facing north, now south. After every such turnabout the outline of a constellation appears reversed and topsy-turvy, which confuses the beginner unless he knows its configuration quite thoroughly.

IN THE COUNTRY the selection of a point of observation is simply a question of vista, but for the city dweller it can be quite a problem. His most serious handicap is the city sky itself, which is but a pallid replica of the country sky because of the dimming effect of the city's floods of light. Conditions somewhat improve late at night, when only street lights remain on. The flat roof of an apartment building is a good spot for observing the sky. If you cannot go to an apartment roof, you will have to resort to a vacant lot or yard. You will do well to protect yourself against the glare of city lights by scanning the sky through a cone made of stiff, dark paper. The cone must not be too narrow, lest your field of view become too small.

If you have a window facing more-or-less south or north and thus more-or-less on the meridian, you have a great advantage, especially in cold weather. You can study the constellations piecemeal, so to speak, for it cannot be overemphasized that our charts are good for any hour all the year round. Whenever you are disposed to do some stargazing, all you have to do is consult the timetables, and they will tell you what circle with its stars and constellations is on the meridian. In time you will become familiar with a number of constellations, and when you go into the open you will find them of great help in identifying others.

Although reliable observers report having seen stars of sixth magnitude in New York City on exceptional evenings, it is generally accepted that fourth magnitude is the limit for a city. Since poor visibility is rather the rule than the exception, the city dweller cannot expect to find an object in a jiffy; his eyes first have to adapt themselves to the dimmed brightnesses of the stars. Much also depends on the magnitudes of the stars forming a constellation's outlines and the elevation of the stars above the horizon. City haze blots out stars near the horizon of second and even of first magnitude. In the city sky a diurnal constellation may always be visible when on the upper northern meridian, but not always when on the lower meridian, i.e., when near the horizon. It sometimes happens, when visibility is thus restricted, that not much more than the area near the zenith is really visible.

In the city sky we often cannot see an entire constellation but only its more prominent stars, and we must conjecture its outlines. The next evening, atmospheric conditions favoring, we may do better. Much depends, of course, on the conditions prevailing at your observation point. In this regard you will be astonished to discover how helpful the above-mentioned observation cone can be. Objects around you, such as a chimney (if you are observing from a rooftop), may also shield you from some glare, enabling you to see otherwise invisible stars.

Thus, if unraveling the maze of the sky is a difficult task by itself, it is all the more so for the city dweller; it requires unusual enthusiasm and perseverance for him. But his pride and satisfaction will be all the greater if he can identity the stars and constellations that are out of reach to the uninitiated and the less diligent.

The city dweller cannot fully come to realize the beauty of the night sky until he visits the country on a clear evening.

In the star-filled sky he may feel the immensity of the heavens and the wonder of being at once insignificant and part of this unfathomable universe.

FINALLY, a few words must be said about the Milky Way as it appears in the sky. It is a rather narrow luminous band of irregular confines encircling the entire celestial sphere. Usually it is only faintly visible, but on exceptionally clear nights it is of awe-inspiring beauty, particularly so to one who understands its nature (see pp. 23–25).

The Milky Way passes through or comes into contact with the following constellations considered in Chapters 4 and 5: Scorpio (pronounced *Skor'pi-o*), Sagittarius, Aquila, Hercules, Lyra, Cygnus, Cepheus, Cassiopeia, Perseus, Andromeda, Auriga, Gemini (pronounced *Jem'i-nī*), and Orion.

(Note that for technical reasons, and because we are here primarily interested in the constellations, the Milky Way is not shown in the charts.)

Notes

Note A *(see p. 33).* The sun is assumed to be on the meridian every day exactly at noon, but actually it is so only four times a year (about mid-April, mid-June, September 1, and Christmas Day); on all other days it is somewhat late or ahead of time. To the naked eye, however, the variation is hardly noticeable. The sun's maximum deviation is only a little more than one-tenth of an interval between two numbered circles on our charts.

We might remember that standard time itself is always ahead of or behind local time, depending on the longitude of our location. This error, too, is negligible. Both our fictitious meridian and our fictitious watch time serve their purposes adequately.

Note B *(see p. 36).* Every two hours a new circle crosses our meridian. As the interval between any two circles is sub-divided into ten decimal units (see the lower horizon-line on Chart II), a new decimal unit crosses the meridian every 12 minutes.

Suppose that it is 10:25 P.M., May 1, but that our watch is 25 minutes slow and shows 10:00 P.M. sharp. Consulting the May 1 row of our timetables we find this hour under circle 10, and we expect to find to the left of our meridian the bright star Spica (pronounced *Spī'ka*) and to the right the constellation Corvus (pronounced *Kor'vus*). Since 25 minutes is equal to about two subdivisions of an interval, all stars will have moved two decimal units to the right of the meridian. Exactly on the meridian, then, will be an imaginary line drawn through point 10.2 on the horizon-line. Clearly, neither Spica nor Corvus will have traveled out of our field of view; hence, we do not bother about minutes.

Note C *(see p. 36).* Circle 1 crosses our meridian at noon January 1 and circle 2 crosses at noon February 1 (one month, or about 30 days, later). Therefore, each succeeding subdivision (decimal unit) of an interval crosses our meridian at noon three days later. Thus, on January 4 circle 1.1 crosses the meridian at noon; on January 7 circle 1.2; on January 22 circle 1.7.

This obviously applies to all months, so we may make the following generalization: *the integer of a circle's numeral indicates the month, and the decimal multiplied by 3, plus 1, indicates the day when this circle is on the meridian at noon.* For instance, the circle of the star Pollux is 7.5 (Chart II), which means that it is on the meridian at noon on July 16 (the seventh month being July and $5 \times 3 + 1$ being 16).

One of the unique features of Chart II is that it gives the daily position of the sun in the sky; Chart II is for this reason an **ephemeris** of the sun. Since each circle of our charts **transits** or crosses the meridian every day almost exactly four minutes earlier than on the previous day, it will transit the

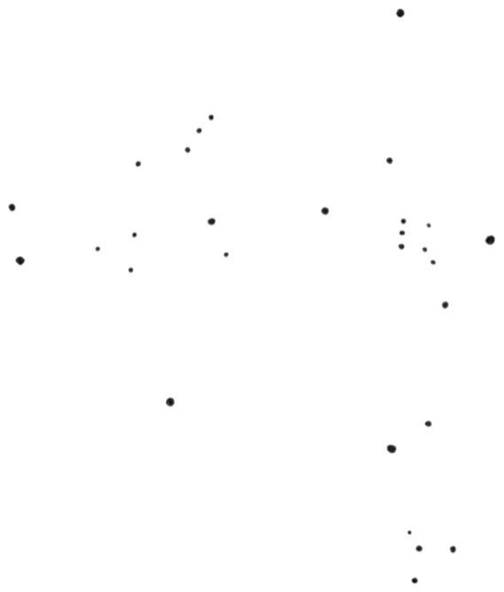

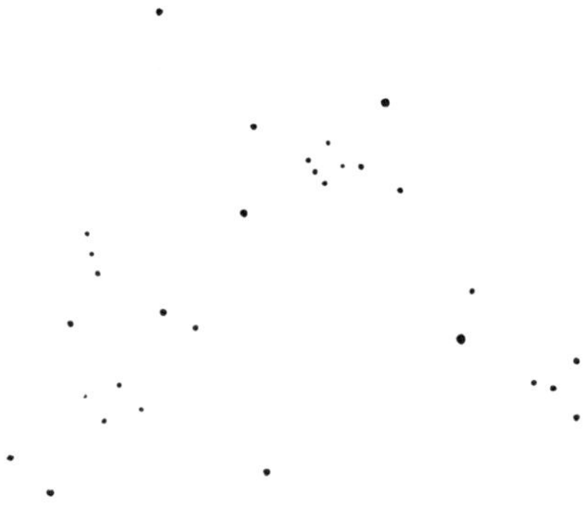

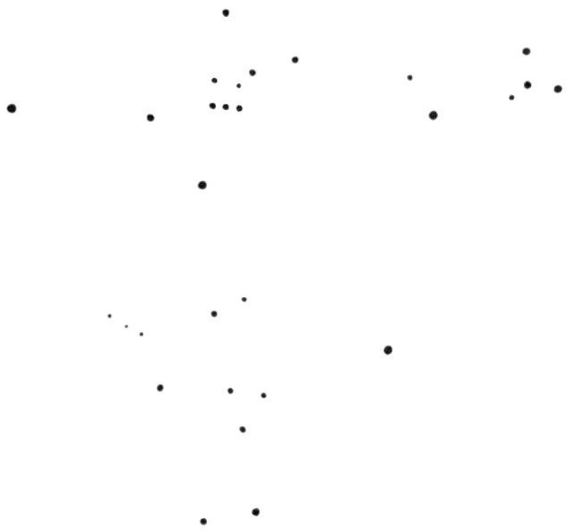

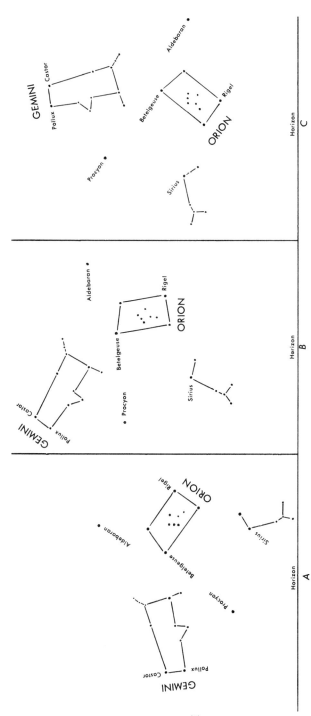

FIG. 4.—Orion: A, three hours before culminating; B, at culmination; C, three hours after culminating. The corresponding upper and lower diagrams are identical, outlines and labels having been added to the lower diagrams to orient the beginner.

47

meridian at noon only once every year. The sun, of course, transits the meridian every day. Thus, the point of intersection of a date's circle with the ecliptic is the sun's place in the sky at noon on that date. For instance, on August 22 (circle 8.7) the sun is on the ecliptic near the star Regulus (pronounced *Rĕg′you-lŭs*), whose circle is also, and always, 8.7.

The same reasoning applies to all hours, not to noon alone. For example, at 11:00 P.M., November 1, circle 4.5 is on the meridian. On November 4, the circle is 4.6, and so on, adding one decimal unit, or 0.1, every three days. Hence, for November 19, 0.6 must be added to 4.5, giving us circle 5.1, practically the same result as that found on p. 37 by the shorter method.

Note D (see p. 39). We have only to remember that in the sky's diurnal movement every circle transits two hours later than the last. For instance, what circle transits at 9:00 P.M. on February 4?

According to the practical rule on p. 37 the circle for noon, February 4, is 2. "Nine P.M." means nine hours or 4.5 intervals after noon; therefore, at 9:00 P.M. circle 2 plus 4.5, or circle 6.5, will transit, with Orion and Auriga.

Note E (see p. 39). The circles of Chart II are arcs of great circles of the celestial sphere. The arcs are oriented to our meridian much as the hour hand of a clock held vertically might be oriented to a minute hand fixed at 12:00.

When **culminating,** or on the meridian, a constellation is highest, brightest, and in its "normal" position, but before culminating, while it is still rising, the constellation is farther from the meridian, lower, and turned to the left. After culminating, while it is setting, the constellation again is farther from the meridian and lower, but it is turned to the right.

We are now in a position to recognize a constellation whether it is rising (in the east) or setting (in the west). To illustrate, suppose it is 11:00 P.M., January 1. On Chart II we find this date and hour under circle 6.5, and we see that the constellation Orion is culminating. Figure 4*B* (p. 47) shows the sky around Orion at 11:00 P.M. Figure 4, *A* and *C* show the same portion of the sky at 8:00 P.M., three hours before Orion's culmination, and at 2:00 A.M., three hours after culmination. The superficial appearances of *A* and *C* are so different that the uninitiated would hardly believe that they represent the same part of the sky.

To identify in the maze of stars a contour that does not exactly conform to the pattern on his chart is a difficult and frustrating task for the novice. For this reason we advise the beginner first to identify and memorize the constellations in their normal positions on the meridian. After becoming familiar with the configurations of the constellations, he will recognize them in any position.

Note F (see p. 41). If the apparent magnitude of a star is numerically one *less* than that of another star, the first is two and one-half times as bright as the second. For example, Polaris is a star of second magnitude, its exact magnitude being 2.2. Spica and Capella (pronounced *Ka-pĕl′a*) are both considered first-magnitude stars; their respective magnitudes are 1.2 and 0.2. Spica, therefore, is two and one-half times as bright as Polaris, and Capella is two and one-half times as bright as Spica.

On a map it is impossible to represent exactly all shades of brightness; therefore, magnitudes are rounded off to the nearest integer. As a consequence, to all magnitudes from 2.51 to 3.50, magnitude 3 is assigned. For this reason star-maps cannot be relied upon as accurate indicators of brightness.

There are 20 stars of first magnitude. Fortunately, 15 of them are visible in our latitudes (see p. 100). On our charts they are represented by large asterisks. Stars of second magnitude appear as smaller asterisks, and stars of third and fourth magnitudes as large and small dots.

With very few exceptions, the patterns of the constellations are formed by stars of the first four magnitudes. Stars of fifth magnitude are, as a rule, omitted from our charts, since they would be of no help in locating and identifying the constellations. Although lucid in the country, fifth-magnitude stars are invisible in the city. Sixth-magnitude stars, too, are visible only in the country, but only on exceptional nights, and to very keen eyes.

Note G (for readers who are acquainted with the rudiments of astronomy). This book is intended for the general reader, but its starmaps can be used to advantage and with convenience by the amateur astronomer and perhaps even by the professional astronomer for solving certain simple problems when great accuracy is not required. For instance, let us determine the times of rising, culminating, and setting for Denebola on April 7.

The calendrical circle of April 7 is 4.2, which means that on this date the sun is on this circle, culminating at noon. Denebola's circle, 9.6 (Chart II), lags behind the sun's by 5.4 circle-intervals (9.6 − 4.2) or 10.8 hours (2 × 5.4) or 10^h 48^m. Denebola will culminate that much later than the sun, at 10:48 P.M.

Denebola rises at culmination time 10:48 P.M. minus its semidiurnal arc and sets at 10:48 P.M. plus the same semidiurnal arc. The amateur astronomer knows how to find the semidiurnal arc, most probably from a table. For Denebola (declination $+15°$), at latitude 40° N., it is 6^h 52^m. On April 7, therefore, Denebola rises at 3:56 P.M. and sets at 5:40 A.M.

If the necessary semidiurnal arc is not at once available, it can be found graphically for stars of declination $+23.5°$ to $−23.5°$. We draw through Denebola a line parallel to the equator. This line will intersect the ecliptic at a point of the same declination as that of Denebola, in our case approximately at calendrical circle 8.3. This is the circle of August 10. On this date the sun rises at 5:05 A.M. and sets at 7:04 P.M., information obtainable from the daily newspapers. The total time the sun remains over the horizon is thus 13^h 59^m. Half of this figure, 7^h 00^m, gives us a second reckoning of the semidiurnal arc. The two values give results that differ by only a few minutes.

4

The Year-Round Constellations (Chart I)

F ACING NORTH, you have before you the circumpolar constellations, therefore you must use Chart I. The observer in Figure 3 (p. 31) faces south; to see the circumpolar constellations he must turn and face north. He will then have before him, a little less than halfway up from the northern horizon to the zenith, the polestar Polaris, which is almost at the center of the northern sky. Polaris is centered on Chart I.

Suppose it is 8:15 P.M. on April 20. Rounding off the time to 8:00 P.M., we find this hour for April 1 above circle 8, but as we are in the third week of April we have to use circle 8.5 (see p. 37). Scanning our upper northern meridian, we find, in accordance with Chart I, no constellations on the meridian itself, but to our right (east) we see the most conspicuous, well-known polar constellation, the Big Dipper. To the right of Polaris we find the Little Dipper. Below Polaris, down near the horizon, are Cepheus and Draco. Some of the stars in these two constellations are invisible, being hidden by the haze near the horizon.

Notice that the circle numerals on Chart I increase from left to right (clockwise), unlike the numerals on Chart II. This is so because we face south when using Chart II and north when using Chart I.

Circumpolar Constellations

The Big Dipper of Ursa Major, the Great
   Bear
The Little Dipper of Ursa Minor, the Little
   Bear
Draco, the Dragon
Cassiopeia, the Queen
Cepheus, the King
Perseus

THE BIG DIPPER is, properly speaking, only an **asterism**—
a group of stars forming part of a constellation—of Ursa Major, the Great Bear. It warrants being referred to as a constellation in its own right, however. Six of the seven stars
that form it are bright stars of second magnitude. The Big
Dipper is one of the few constellations that really looks like
what it is supposed to represent; it does look like a dipper!
   Strangely, many ancient peoples have called Ursa Major a
bear, even the Indians of North America, who lived very far
indeed from the ancient Chaldea, the birthplace of constellation names. In England, however, it is called either Arthur's
or Charles's Wain (Wagon), or the Plow. In splendor it is
surpassed only by Orion (see p. 96).
   The Big Dipper is as useful as it is beautiful. A line drawn
from star Beta to star Alpha and extended about five times
their distance from each other will almost hit Polaris, which
practically coincides with the pole of the northern celestial
hemisphere. These two stars are for this reason called The
Pointers.
   Of the other stars of the Big Dipper, the star at the bend
of the handle, which the Arabs named Mizar, should be mentioned. Mizar is not so interesting for itself as for a faint star
very close to it called Alcor ("the weak one") or Saidak ("the
test"). The Arabs are said to have used this star as a test of
good vision for their soldiers. Mizar, in its own right, is a
genuine binary (see p. 20) and was one of the first binaries

to be photographed. With Alcor it forms, in addition, an optical double (see p. 20). As you look at Mizar and Alcor, which seem so close together, you might remember that light takes about three months to travel from one to the other.

It is of interest to note that binary systems afford astronomers the only direct method for determining the masses of the two stars concerned; for single stars they have to rely upon more indirect methods that involve some uncertainty.

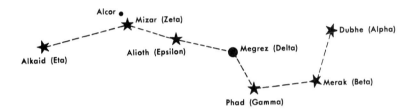

Fig. 5.—The Big Dipper. The individual stars of the older, widely known constellations were often given names. For purposes of cataloguing, another system is now used: the most prominent star of the constellation is called Alpha (the first letter in the Greek alphabet), the second Beta, and so on. The Big Dipper is unusual in that its seven major stars are listed in regular order following the Greek alphabet (contrast the scheme for Orion; see p. 95). When a constellation includes more stars than the 24 letters of the Greek alphabet, we use numbers, for example, "61 Cygni," meaning star number 61 of the constellation Cygnus.

With the exceptions of stars Alpha and Eta, the stars of the Big Dipper move in space in the same direction, as if they belonged to one family, which, literally, is the case. What may be even more astonishing is the fact that Sirius, in a very different constellation, is a member of the same family! Such family groups are known as **galactic clusters**. We know that these stars belong together because our measurements show that all of them have identical motions. Alpha and Eta, however, move in a different direction. As a consequence, one day the Big Dipper will no longer be recognizable as a dipper. We need not anticipate that day too anxiously, however; it will be thousands of years before the slightest change in the familiar shape of the Big Dipper will be perceptible to the naked eye.

The Big Dipper spreads from circle 9 to circle 11. From the dates and hours of circle 11 we conclude that it is highest in the sky in the spring, during the early evening hours.

There are many interesting objects in Ursa Major other than the Big Dipper, but they are revealed only by the telescope or the camera. Of the many galaxies to be found within the boundaries of this constellation, two typical ones are shown on the following pages. Both are galaxies still "in the making." The first is supposed to be in an earlier stage of development because of its strongly marked spiral form. It lies near the end of the Big Dipper's handle, not far from Mizar. This galaxy is comparatively near us—for a galaxy. It is only about 2.5 million light-years away. The second galaxy lies beyond star Alpha. They are both among the objects that the famous comet-hunter Messier listed in 1784 as curious but unimportant to the work of locating comets. They are known as M 101 and M 81, or in the *New General Catalogue* as NGC 5457 and NGC 3031. Today, such galaxies are studied intensively to gain information concerning the structure and behavior of the universe.

FROM THE ASTRONOMER'S POINT OF VIEW, the most important of the polar constellations—because it includes Polaris —is the Little Dipper, an asterism of the constellation Ursa Minor, the Little Bear. The Little Dipper, too, actually looks like a dipper, but it is far less conspicuous than the Big Dipper. It has only two bright stars (of second magnitude), Polaris and Kochab; the remaining five are rather faint, so that the Little Dipper is clearly visible only on clear nights. Kochab and its nearest neighbor of the bowl are called the Guardians, or Wardens, of the Pole.

Although Polaris's apparent magnitude is only 2.2, it is intrinsically several thousand times as bright as our sun; it is

Photograph from the Mt. Wilson and Palomar Observatories

SPIRAL GALAXY (M 101)
IN URSA MAJOR

Photograph from the Mt. Wilson and Palomar Observatories

SPIRAL GALAXY (M 81)
IN URSA MAJOR

dimmed by its great distance, 270 light-years. It is a Cepheid variable (see p. 59), but the fluctuations in its brightness are too small to be observed by the naked eye.

The four stars forming the bowl of the Little Dipper are of second (Kochab), third, fourth, and fifth magnitudes. On a really clear evening—unfortunately, not a common occurrence—you will be able to see all of them and thus form a true notion of stellar magnitudes.

The Little Dipper is, of course, a year-round constellation. Its bowl is highest in the sky during the early evening hours in midsummer.

DRACO, THE DRAGON, is a rather pallid constellation. To some people, its contour, as shown on the chart, really suggests a dragon. Others can see no resemblance whatsoever.

Draco is now chiefly of historical interest, because one of its stars, Thuban, was the polestar about 5,000 years ago, at the time when the Egyptian Pharaohs were building their great pyramids and temples. At that time, from the bottom of the long, tubelike passageways of several of the pyramids, the Egyptians could see Thuban. These passageways [1] may be compared to the tubes of telescopes. This and other structural peculiarities of the pyramids have led many to surmise that they served, in part, as primitive observatories. Centuries ago Thuban was much brighter than it is at present and, possibly, it was brighter still when it was the polestar.

You may be surprised by our statement that 5,000 years ago the earth had another polestar instead of Polaris. This was the case because the axis of the earth slowly changes its direction, and in 26,000 years describes a complete cone. This motion is called **precession.** In about A.D. 28,000 Polaris again will be the polestar; in the meantime, other stars will become polestars: around A.D. 14,000, the brilliant star Vega, and around A.D. 23,000, Thuban again.

[1] The passageway of the pyramid of Cheops (3,000 B.C.) is over 300 feet long.

Thuban lies roughly midway between Mizar of the Big Dipper and Kochab[2] of the Little Dipper. Although it slightly outshines the stars in its immediate neighborhood, it is, nevertheless, rather faint (of fourth magnitude). It culminates at 8:00 P.M. around July 1 and at 9:00 P.M. around June 16 (circle 11).

Finding Draco is difficult for the beginner, as its stars are rather faint. The only bright star, Etamin ("the dragon's head") is of second magnitude. The other stars outlining the dragon's head, a quadrangle, are of second, third, fourth, and fifth magnitudes. Like the stars forming the bowl of the Little Dipper, they display a fine gamut of stellar magnitudes, but are fully observable only when visibility is really good. Etamin culminates at 9:00 P.M. around August 1 and at 8:00 P.M. around August 16 (circle 12.5).

RIVALING THE BIG DIPPER in prominence is the constellation Cassiopeia. It is almost directly opposite the Big Dipper and is therefore an autumn and winter constellation. It lies in the Milky Way and its contour resembles a distended M or W, depending on its position in the sky.

In Greek mythology Cassiopeia was the wife of Cepheus, King of Ethiopia. Overproud of her beauty and of that of her daughter Andromeda, she boasted so much that she offended the Nereids, the attendants of Poseidon, god of the seas. Poseidon sent a sea monster to ravage Ethiopia's seacoasts and demanded the sacrifice of Andromeda, who was promptly chained to a rock to be devoured by the sea monster. In the nick of time the hero Perseus, riding the winged horse Pegasus, killed the sea monster and married Andromeda. Thus everything ended happily, and all the actors of the myth were put into the sky.

Cepheus and Perseus are circumpolar constellations; Andromeda and Pegasus we shall encounter when we discuss

---

[2] "Kochab" means "the star," i.e., "the polestar," in Arabic. It actually was the polestar about 500 B.C.

the autumn constellations. Cassiopeia culminates at 8:00 P.M. around December 1 and at 7:00 P.M. around December 16 (circle 4).

CEPHEUS is a rather inconspicuous constellation; it has not a single star of first or second magnitude. It is, therefore, rather difficult to find among its surrounding stars. Its outlines are a combination of an almost-square quadrangle and a triangle. Some people see in it a church belfry and spire. If you want to locate Cepheus, watch its stars 1 and 2 culminate simultaneously (circle 2.2) on October 1 at 8:00 P.M.

Star Delta of Cepheus is famous as the prototype of a class of genuine variables (see p. 21) called **Cepheid variables.** Delta Cephei, as it is known among astronomers, changes in magnitude from 3.6 to 4.3 and back to 3.6 in a regular period of 5 days 8 hours 48 minutes. It is a double star about 1,300 light-years away from us. It is far beyond the scope of this book to explain how it is done, but owing to this and other Cepheid variables, astronomers can now determine with reasonable accuracy the distances of star systems outside our own galaxy.

CASSIOPEIA'S SON-IN-LAW PERSEUS also lies in the Milky Way and is therefore readily located. If you can see Cassiopeia but not Perseus, be patient; in an hour or so Perseus will become visible.

This constellation involves quite a few stars, but most prominent are the three stars forming part of the "segment of Perseus," including Marfak (also called Algenib) and Algol, the classical variable star or, more correctly, eclipsing binary. Algol, the Winking Demon, varies in brightness from magnitude 2.2 to magnitude 3.4 in a very regular period of 69 hours. Once in each revolution the larger, but fainter, of the pair partially eclipses the brighter star, the eclipse lasting for about ten hours. It is a very interesting and rewarding sight to watch.

If you have difficulty in locating Perseus as an entirety,

watch for the culmination of either Marfak or Algol alone (circles 5.3 and 5.2).

On Chart I two more constellations are indicated: Auriga and Cygnus. They properly belong to the circumpolar constellations, and their respective principal stars Capella and Deneb are beneath the horizon for only four to five hours every day. We can see them any evening if we have the patience to wait, late into the night if need be, for their appearance. They are on the chart for purposes of orientation, as links between the circumpolar and the seasonal constellations.

5

The Seasonal Constellations (Chart II)

THE SEASONAL CONSTELLATIONS are classified as spring, summer, autumn, and winter constellations. This classification indicates the season during which a given constellation is most conveniently observed; it does not mean that a winter constellation is visible only in the winter. In order to be consistent, we shall call spring constellations, for example, only those which culminate at a convenient hour, say 8:00 P.M., in the spring (for midsummer this hour may be somewhat early, as twilight continues almost to 9:00 P.M. in June and July).

Naturally, a constellation is also visible during the preceding and subsequent seasons, but its hours of culmination are respectively later or earlier in the evening, as can be seen from the dates and hours on Chart II.

Most propitious for illustrating this variation is the winter constellation Orion, whose visibility in the sky we shall study as an example of how to make use of our circles. From circle 6.5 we see that Orion is on the meridian at about 8:00 P.M. on February 16, i.e., in the winter, as required by our stipulation for a winter constellation. However, Orion rises six hours earlier, at 2:00 P.M. It remains invisible until about 7:00 P.M., when, on February 16, twilight ends. Since it sets six hours

61

after culminating, at 2:00 A.M., Orion is visible for seven hours.

Examining the dates and hours of circle 6.5 for autumn and spring, say November 16 and April 16, we find that in autumn Orion culminates at 2:00 A.M. It rises, consequently, at 8:00 P.M. and sets at 8:00 A.M. Thus it is visible from 8:00 P.M. to about 6:00 A.M. (when twilight begins), or for ten hours, even longer than on February 16. The drawback for the viewer is that a constellation is in its normal and most favorable viewing position when it is on or near the meridian, in this case from about midnight to 4:00 A.M., rather late for the average stargazer. By our criterion, then, Orion cannot be considered an autumn constellation.

On April 16 Orion culminates at 4:00 P.M. but does not become visible until about 8:00 P.M. It sets at about 10:00 P.M.; consequently, we can see it for only two hours, and only while it is setting, i.e., while it is low, turned down, and not wholly visible. Orion is certainly not a spring constellation.

The reader must be warned not to conclude that all stars and constellations rise six hours before culminating and set six hours after culminating, and are thus twelve hours above and twelve hours below the horizon. This holds good only for stars or constellations exactly on the celestial equator, as Orion happens to be. Stars lower in the sky than the equator are above the horizon for fewer than twelve hours: the farther below the celestial equator they are, the shorter the period they are visible. Conversely, stars higher than the equator stay above the horizon for more than twelve hours. Many of the circumpolar stars never go below the horizon at all.

Spring Constellations

Leo, the Lion
Gemini, the Twins
Canis Minor, the Lesser Dog
Cancer, the Crab

Boötes, the Bear Driver or Plowman
Virgo, the Virgin
Hydra, the Sea Serpent
Corvus, the Crow
Coma Berenices, Berenice's Hair

THE OUTSTANDING spring constellation is Leo, the Lion. Its principal star, Regulus, is at the end of the so-called Sickle, which is formed by Regulus and five other stars of second to fifth magnitude. This asterism is unmistakable. The Sickle is supposed to be the lion's head with its mane. The star Denebola (pronounced *De-neb'o-la*) is Leo's tail.

Although intrinsically Regulus is about 178 times brighter than the sun and Sirius about 23 times brighter, Regulus is much fainter than Sirius. The difference in apparent brightness is due, of course, to the difference in distance: Regulus is 85 light-years away from us, Sirius only 8.7.

Regulus is one of the Royal Stars of ancient Persian astrology. About 4,000 years ago the sun was to be found in the constellation Taurus at the spring equinox, in Leo at the summer solstice, in Scorpio at the autumn equinox, and in Aquarius at the winter solstice. These were the first signs of the zodiac, later expanded to twelve. The brightest star in each constellation was designated a Royal Star: Aldebaran (circle 5.9), Regulus (circle 8.7), Antares (circle 11.9), and Fomalhaut (pronounced *Fō'mal-oh;* circle 3.1). Their circle values are roughly 6, 9, 12, and 3, so the year was divided quite closely into four equal seasons.

Regulus culminates at 8:00 P.M. around April 21 (circle 8.7). When culminating, Regulus is rather high in the sky, being well above the celestial equator. It is almost exactly on the ecliptic. Ironically, Regulus, meaning "the little king," is the least bright of the 20 first-magnitude stars.

Although Leo is the foremost spring constellation, it is visible, earlier or later in the evening, for eight months. It is one of the twelve constellations, called **zodiacal constellations,** that lie on the ecliptic.

GEMINI, THE TWINS, with its two principal stars, Pollux and Castor, is also prominent among the spring constellations. Its contour reminds one of a crude silhouette of an upright piano. Pollux is yellow; Castor, white. At present Pollux is the brighter star, but centuries ago Castor was the brighter of the two. According to Greek mythology, Castor and Pollux were the sons of Zeus and Leda, whom Zeus visited in the guise of a swan. They were the brothers of the beautiful Helen of Troy.

In ancient times Castor and Pollux were worshiped as the patrons of travelers by sea. Some people regard the exclamation "by Jiminy" to be the corrupted form of a conjectural sailors' oath, "by Gemini."

In early spring Castor and Pollux are already high in the sky during the early evening hours; around the vernal equinox, March 21, they culminate just before 8:00 P.M. (circle 7.5).

By a curious coincidence, two of the three planets discovered in our era, Uranus (by Herschel in 1781) and Pluto (by Tombaugh in 1930), were first observed in this constellation. Gemini is another of the twelve zodiacal constellations.

BELOW POLLUX is another bright star, Procyon, of the constellation Canis Minor, the Lesser Dog. We have already referred to Procyon in connection with its dwarf companion of fabulous density (see p. 10). Procyon is several times brighter, intrinsically, than our sun. It is one of our nearest neighbors, being only 11 light-years away. It received its name from the fact that it rises in the east earlier than the famous Sirius, the Dog Star; "Procyon" means "before the dog" in Greek.

Procyon is but slightly higher in the sky than the celestial equator; it culminates at 8:00 P.M. about March 15 (circle 7.5). Canis Minor is, strictly speaking, rather a late-winter constellation, according to our classification, but Procyon is too conspicuous in the early evening hours of spring to be passed over when we are considering the vernal sky.

BETWEEN POLLUX AND REGULUS lies Cancer, the Crab, the most inconspicuous of all the zodiacal constellations. Its outlines resemble an inverted, asymmetrical Y. Near its center is a hazy spot—you may be able to see it by using averted vision—called the Beehive. A small telescope resolves the Beehive into a stellar cluster.

However faint, Cancer can easily be identified at 8:00 P.M. around April 1 (circle 8). Cancer would hardly warrant mention were it not another of the twelve zodiacal constellations.

BOÖTES (pronounced *Bo-ō'-teez*), the Bear Driver or Plowman (his plow being the Big Dipper) is a late spring or early summer constellation. Its principal star, Arcturus (pronounced *Ark-tōō'rus*), is the first star to become visible high in the sky in late spring and early summer. Although you will have no difficulty identifying Arcturus using Chart II, you can also find it by continuing the curve formed by the Big Dipper's handle until you hit this exceptionally brilliant yellowish star. It is surpassed in brightness, but only slightly surpassed, by just one summer star, Vega (pronounced *Vē'ga*) of the constellation Lyra, the Lyre (see p. 77). Vega, however, is far away from Arcturus and of a decidedly bluish tinge, so a mix-up is most unlikely.

When reading of brilliant yellows and bluish tinges, do not build up expectations of single, steady star colors. Stars are often called "red," "bloody," "yellow," or "blue," and through the telescope we can see that they actually are those colors. To the naked eye, however, the coloration is not so noticeable. Much depends on atmospheric conditions and on the acuteness of the observer's vision.

Arcturus makes the rest of the constellation's stars seem dim, yet the contour of the Bear Driver is easily discernible, reminding one of an elongated kite.

Arcturus is over 10,000 times larger in volume than the sun and is about 36 light-years away from us. It is called "the runaway star," because it races through space at about 100 miles per second, faster than any other lucid star. Another of the

names by which Arcturus is popularly known, "Job's Star,"
is derived from a reference to it in Chapter 38 of the Book
of Job. This interesting star culminates at 8:00 P.M. around
June 21 (circle 10.8).

IF WE CONTINUE the curve we were drawing from the Big
Dipper in order to locate Arcturus, we meet another conspicuous star, Spica, of the late-spring constellation Virgo
(pronounced *Vur'go*), the Virgin. Spica is rather isolated
among several insignificant stars. To the naked eye only Spica
is really noticeable; you can readily locate this star without
identifying the constellation to which it belongs. For this
reason a discussion of the outlines of Virgo can be omitted.
Virgo has the distinction, at least, of being a zodiacal constellation.

Spica is white and rather remote, about 150 light-years
away. At 8:00 P.M. it culminates around June 10 (circle
10.3).

Within the boundaries of Virgo lies the Realm of Galaxies
with a **supergalaxy** composed of several hundred spirals
similar to those of Ursa Major, shown on pp. 55 and 56. The
position of this supergalaxy is a little to the left (east) of
Denebola of Leo.

Not within the Realm of Galaxies but just west of Spica,
almost exactly on circle 10, the camera reveals another spiral
galaxy, turned to us edgewise. It is reproduced on the following page. Although its superb glow is the combined light
of billions of suns like ours, it required an exposure of over
eight hours to take this picture of it, so great is its distance
(7 million light-years).

Remember that all galaxies, except one in the constellation
Andromeda, are invisible, not only to the naked eye, but
often even to the most powerful telescopes. We must rely on
sensitive photographic emulsions to register their images.
The positions of a few of them are indicated at appropriate
places in our discussion in the belief that by trying to locate
them mentally, we shall better retain them in our memories

Photograph from the Mt. Wilson and Palomar Observatories

SPIRAL GALAXY IN VIRGO, SEEN EDGE-ON

and we can also more readily appreciate their awe-inspiring nature.

THE LONG, wandering constellation Hydra, the Sea Serpent, is barely worth mentioning, as its stars, with the exception of Alphard, are faint and of little interest. Alphard, of second magnitude, lies below and a little to the right (west) of Regulus. Regulus, Alphard, and Procyon form an almost right-angled triangle, with Alphard at the right angle. The outlines of Hydra are so faint and extended that they are of no help in identifying Alphard, which is distinct by itself in its immediate neighborhood. Its very name, meaning "the solitary one," implies the paucity of stars around it.

Alphard, of reddish hue, is supposed to represent the Sea Serpent's heart. It culminates at 8:00 P.M. about April 10 (circle 8.3).

CORVUS, THE CROW, is not particularly interesting but it is relatively well defined. Its four principal stars, all third magnitude, form an irregular quadrangle. Even on an average night it is rather conspicuous, not being beset with many surrounding stars. It lies a little below and to the right (west) of Spica, of Virgo, and it culminates one hour before Spica (circles 9.8 and 10.3).

FOR THE BENEFIT of readers with particularly good vision another late-spring constellation should be mentioned, namely, Coma Berenices, Berenice's Hair. It is situated just above an imaginary line connecting Arcturus and Denebola, closer to the latter, near circle 10. To the average eye it appears as a haze, except possibly on an unusually clear night and when averted vision is applied. An ordinary opera glass resolves this haze into a swarm of stars.

The myth connected with this constellation is that Berenice, wife of an Egyptian king, in fulfillment of a vow deposited her beautiful hair on the altar as a sacrifice. To everyone's consternation, however, the hair had disappeared by the

Photograph from the Mt. Wilson and Palomar Observatories

A CLUSTER OF GALAXIES
IN COMA BERENICES

Photograph from the Mt. Wilson and Palomar Observatories

A SPIRAL GALAXY
IN COMA BERENICES

next morning. Scandal was averted by the declaration of the quick-witted high priest that the gods had taken the hair to heaven to perpetuate it in the form of this constellation.

The Realm of Galaxies in Virgo extends into Coma Berenices. The striking photograph on the preceding page shows one of these galaxies. Its resemblance to the edgewise view of the schematic sketch of the Milky Way galaxy on p. 24 is immediately apparent. Measurements have shown that its size is of the same order of magnitude as that of the Milky Way. Our galaxy might look as glorious to an observer somewhere in this distant galaxy in Coma Berenices as his galaxy looks to us.

The circumpolar Big Dipper may also be called a spring constellation, since it is highest in the sky and in full view (inverted) at 8:00 P.M. around June 1 (circle 10, Chart I).

Summer Constellations

Corona Borealis, the Northern Crown
Scorpio, the Scorpion
Sagittarius, the Archer
Hercules, or the Kneeler
Ophiuchus, the Serpent Bearer
Libra, the Scales
Lyra, the Lyre
Cygnus, the Swan, or the Northern Cross
Aquila, the Eagle
Delphinus, the Dolphin

To THE LEFT (east) of the upper half of Boötes, the Bear Driver, lies Corona Borealis (pronounced *Ko-rō'na Bō-re-ā'lis*), the Northern Crown. It is not very prominent, as it has only one star of second magnitude, the others being of fourth magnitude. It is, nonetheless, easily distinguished and interesting because it is small, hence concentrated. Corona Borealis forms an almost perfect half-circle, with its principle star Gemma ("the pearl") in the middle. Gemma is also known by its Arabic name, Alphecca ("the bright one"). Again, although only of second apparent magnitude, Gemma is actually 60 times as bright as the sun, its comparative faintness being due to its great distance (80 light-years). Gemma culminates at 8:00 P.M. in mid-July. It is then almost directly overhead (circle 11.5).

To some people Corona Borealis suggests a saucepan without a handle.

NOT VERY HIGH above the horizon and a little to the left (east) of culminating Corona Borealis is a bright, reddish star of first magnitude, surrounded, when the horizon is very heavy, by a rosy halo. This is the remarkable Antares of the constellation Scorpio, the Scorpion.

Not long ago Antares was thought to be the largest of the giant stars, but at present several other stars are known to be much larger. Its volume is, nevertheless, 60 million times that of our sun, and it is 30 to 40 times more massive than the sun. Although Antares is some 2,240 times brighter than the sun, because of its enormous size, its surface luminosity is only one-hundredth that of our parent star.

Antares means "rival of Mars," because Mars, too, is reddish in color. Because the eye is not very susceptible to the red rays of light emitted by Antares, the white star Sirius outshines it 13 times. Otherwise Antares would outshine Sirius considerably. Antares culminates between 8:00 P.M. and 9:00 P.M. around mid-July (circle 11.8).

Scorpio is one of the most impressive summer constellations, even in our latitudes, where it is comparatively low over the horizon and the brilliance of its many stars is dimmed by the heavier atmosphere. It is, however, of striking beauty when viewed from the southern part of the United States, where it appears higher above the horizon. Its outlines are supposed to suggest a scorpion, with Antares its heart. This imaginary scorpion lies just at the edge of the Milky Way, into which its tail plunges deep. Scorpio is one of the twelve zodiacal constellations. It was this scorpion that stung the boastful Orion to death.

SCORPIO'S IMMEDIATE EASTERN NEIGHBOR is the zodiacal constellation Sagittarius, the Archer. It is less striking than
Scorpio, yet prominent enough to be noticed at once. Only
the most vivid imagination, however, can see in this constellation a resemblance to the bow-wielding centaur it is supposed
to represent. Its outstanding features are the Milk Dipper,
consisting of five rather bright stars reminding one of an inverted dipper, and a triangle a little westward (to the right).
If, by the way, you picture the Milk Dipper as if it were after
milk from the Milky Way, you have pointed it in the wrong
direction. The handle's tip is in the Milky Way but the bowl
is outside.

There is not very much more for the naked eye in Sagittarius, except that here the Milky Way is its richest in number
of stars. It is believed that in this direction lies the center
around which our galaxy revolves.

Sagittarius is a rather late summer constellation; the Milk
Dipper culminates more than two hours later than Antares,
between 10:00 P.M. and 11:00 P.M. at the end of July. At 8:00
P.M. it culminates around September 1 (circle 1).

To THE LEFT (east) of Corona Borealis and to the right of
Vega you will find a widespread but rather undistinguished
constellation at or near the zenith during the earlier hours of
midsummer. This constellation is Hercules, or, originally, the
Kneeler.

The starting point most often recommended for the identification of Hercules is the "keystone" formed by its stars 3,
4, 7, and 8. A better way, however, is to look for the crude H
formed by stars 2, 3, 4, 7, 8, and 9. For the beginner it is somewhat difficult to locate these stars, since they are only slightly
brighter than their numerous neighbors. In addition, Hercules
stretches over a great area, and this, too, is confusing. But if
you continue the curve of the stars of Corona Borealis to the
left, you will hit the waistline of Hercules, whose outlines
suggest a one-armed man standing on his head with his legs
astride. The head is the star Ras Algethi ("the kneeler's

head"), which is one of the largest of the red giants, rivaling Antares. Its surface temperature is only 5,000° F., and most of the rays it emits are invisible. This is the reason for its modest appearance; otherwise, it would be one of the most brilliant stars in the sky. In this respect, too, it is similar to Antares.

Ras Algethi culminates at 8:00 P.M. around August 10 (circle 12.3). It is easiest to identify Hercules when Ras Algethi is in transit (culminating). Hercules is then at the zenith.

The photographs so far reproduced in this chapter have been of external galaxies far outside our galaxy, in contradistinction to star clusters which belong to the Milky Way galaxy. Star clusters are of two principal types: **galactic clusters** in the plane of our galaxy containing relatively few stars (50–200) and **globular clusters** in a halo around our galaxy containing many thousands of stars. In addition, there are vast collections of gas—true nebulae—which may be dark or, if a near-by star shines on them, bright.

One of the most famous globular clusters is in Hercules. It was discovered in 1716 by the English astronomer Edmund Halley. Being 30,000 light-years away, only the larger stars of the cluster can be detected by our instruments. The number even of these stars runs into tens of thousands; the total number must be in the hundreds of thousands.

After you have mastered Hercules you can easily locate its globular cluster, even though it is just on the borderline of naked-eye visibility, magnitude 6. It lies on the line connecting stars 7 and 8, nearer to the former.

OPHIUCHUS (pronounced *Off-i-you'kus*), the Serpent Bearer, is also a huge constellation. It looks like an immense elongated quadrangle with a triangle on top of it. The resulting pentagon is approximately bisected by the celestial equator. Its principal star Ras Alhague ("head of the serpent bearer") appears virtually to touch Ras Algethi of Hercules, and the bearer's feet (not shown on the chart) are just above An-

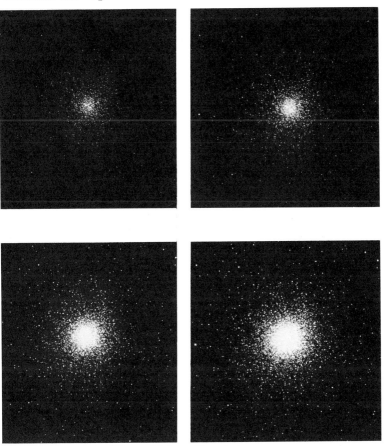

Photographs from the Mt. Wilson and Palomar Observatories

GLOBULAR STAR CLUSTER IN HERCULES

Four exposures of increasing duration
show an increase of one magnitude
on succeeding photographs

tares. The serpent itself is faint and insignificant; only its head (a small triangle) is more-or-less conspicuous, below the star Gemma of Corona Borealis.

Although vast, the Serpent Bearer has no remarkable features. Ras Alhague is of second magnitude and culminates at 8:00 P.M. around August 15 (circle 12.4).

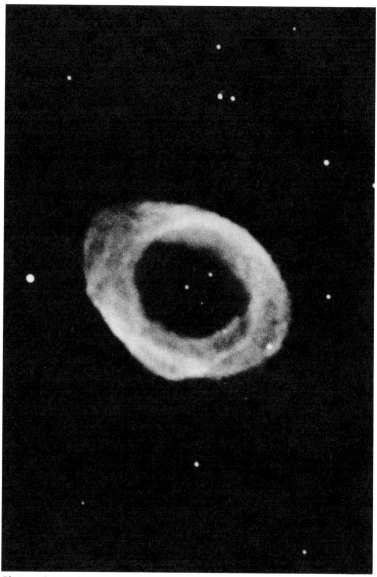

Photograph from the Mt. Wilson and Palomar Observatories

THE "RING" NEBULA,
A PLANETARY NEBULA
IN LYRA

According to some authors Ophiuchus represents the god of medicine, Aesculapius, who attempted to revive Orion after he was stung by the scorpion.

STILL LESS CONSPICUOUS is the constellation Libra (pronounced Lī'bra), the Scales, which lies nearly midway between Antares and Spica, nearer the former. Libra is characterized by four rather faint stars forming an almost square quadrangle. The lowest of these four stars (star 3 on the chart) is a variable that periodically drops to fifth magnitude, at which time it becomes almost invisible.

If you are very anxious to locate Libra, its brightest star (star 1 on the chart) is in transit around July 10 at 8:00 P.M. (circle 11.3).

Libra is one of the twelve zodiacal constellations, and therefore it lies on the ecliptic, the apparent path traveled by the sun. At the autumnal equinox, when the days and nights are of equal length, the sun passes in front of Libra; this may be the reason why scales were chosen to represent this constellation.

THE DOMINANT STAR of the late summer sky is the brilliant Vega of Lyra, the Lyre, the outlines of which have nothing in common with its name and can be passed over. Vega is brilliant enough to be identified by itself; it is surpassed in brilliance only by the winter star Sirius. Its intrinsic brightness is about 56 times that of the sun and over twice that of Sirius, but it is also three times as far from us as is Sirius. Vega is the queen of the late summer sky. Throughout the summer it stays above the horizon about 18 hours every day, and except in late winter (February and March) it can be seen every evening if the observer has patience enough to wait until late into the night. It rises in the northeast and sets in the northwest. When in transit (circle 1) it is almost exactly at the zenith.

Vega is intensely white with a bluish hue, indications of a very high surface temperature. It is interesting to compare the coloration of Vega with that of Antares and Arcturus, which are reddish and yellow respectively. The most propitious time for such a comparison is in July and the first half of August. Vega then is high in the sky, at or near the zenith; Antares is low and near the meridian; and Arcturus is in the southwest.

Vega will be our polestar around A.D. 14,000, and it is the region near Vega toward which our solar system is racing at a speed of 12 miles per second.

Another fine example of an eclipsing binary is Beta Lyrae, which can be observed visually to rise to its magnitude of 3.4 and fall to 4.1 in a period of 12 days, 21 hours, 45 minutes. The masses of the two components are 21 and 10 times the mass of the sun and their diameters are 36 and 28 times the diameter of the sun, yet their distance from each other is only one-third that between the earth and the sun. The two stars are almost in contact!

VEGA is near the Milky Way, but its neighbor, the constellation Cygnus, the Swan, is completely in it. More often and more appropriately Cygnus is called the Northern Cross,[1] because a cross is what it actually resembles. At its top is the first-magnitude star Deneb and at its base the much fainter Albireo. Deneb surpasses our sun 6,000 times in luminosity and is about 1,600 light-years distant; it is the remotest of all first-magnitude stars. Albireo is one of the most beautiful doubles in the sky, one of its components being a rich gold, the other blue; but, alas, these colors can be seen only through a telescope. This part of the Milky Way rivals the region around Sagittarius in richness of stars and contains many extremely interesting nebulae, which are, unfortunately, beyond the reach of the naked eye. The camera, of course, reveals many of these nebulae in their full glory.

The Northern Cross and its surroundings are shown on p. 79, and on the following pages are close-ups of the so-called

[1] There is also a Southern Cross, in the southern celestial hemisphere.

Yerkes Observatory Photograph

THE MILKY WAY IN CYGNUS
OR THE NORTHERN CROSS

The arrow points to the "Filamentary" or "Network" Nebula.
The "North American" Nebula is in the upper left, near Deneb.

North America Nebula—note its resemblance to an outline
of the continent—and the Filamentary or Network Nebula.
On the first picture the North America Nebula is easily recognized in the upper left corner, near Deneb. The Network is in
the lower left; it is indicated by an arrow.

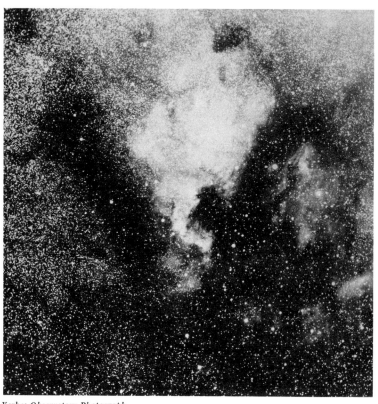

Yerkes Observatory Photograph

THE "NORTH AMERICAN" NEBULA
IN CYGNUS

Albireo of the Northern Cross cannot be seen on the first
picture, since the photograph does not quite include the
whole cross. Not very far from the center of the cross lies the
very faint but renowned star 61 Cygni (star number 61 of the

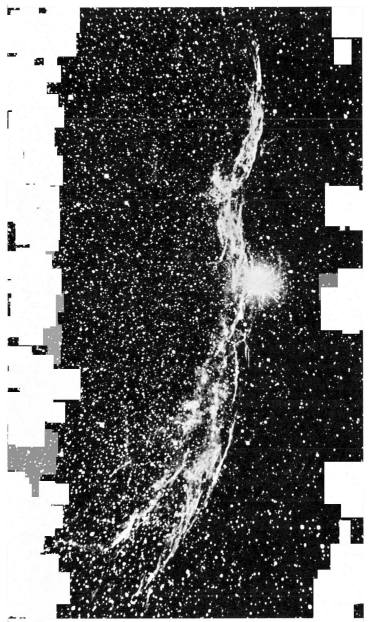

Yerkes Observatory Photograph

THE "FILAMENTARY" OR "NETWORK" NEBULA IN CYGNUS

constellation Cygnus). It will always be remembered because it was the first star the distance of which was measured (by Bessel in 1838), ushering in a new and glorious era of astronomy. It is about 11 light-years away and originally was considered the nearest star. Now, however, a dozen stars are known to be nearer than 61 Cygni.

When culminating, the Northern Cross is at the zenith and Deneb is a little north of the zenith. It is uncomfortable to look at this constellation facing either south or north. When the observer changes from south to north, the outlines reverse, as was pointed out on p. 42. Moreover, when on the meridian, the Northern Cross is somewhat askew and does not resemble a cross, as it does when it is lower in the southwest, about three hours after culmination.

According to our classification, the Northern Cross is an early-autumn constellation, as Deneb culminates at 8:00 P.M. around October 1 (circle 2), but it is better to consider it together with Lyra, since it is a close neighbor of the latter. Ultimately, the Northern Cross, like Lyra, is an almost year-round constellation.

Aquila, the Eagle, is also a late-summer constellation. Its principal star, Altair, alone is of interest to the unaided eye. Altair is easily located on the eastern edge of the Milky Way below the Northern Cross. Its striking brilliance is exceeded only by Vega and Arcturus at this time of the year. Altair is flanked by two much fainter stars, the three forming an almost straight line. Intensely white, it is intrinsically ten times as bright as our sun. Altair is approximately 15 light-years away. It culminates at 8:00 P.M. around September 15 (circle 1.5), rather high in the sky.

The three stars, Vega, Deneb, and Altair are often referred to as the "Summer Triangle."

Delphinus (pronounced *Del-fī'nus*), the Dolphin, lies to the left of Altair, outside the Milky Way. It bears no resemblance whatever to a dophin, being just a small lozenge of four stars with one star as a short tail. Delphinus is faint yet quite distinct. Its visibility is due partly to the fact that its neighborhood is rather empty of lucid stars and partly to the fact that our eyes encompass small constellations more readily than large ones.

Delphinus is also called Job's Coffin. It culminates at 8:00 P.M. around October 1 (circle 2).

OF THE CIRCUMPOLAR CONSTELLATIONS, the Little Dipper (pp. 54–57) is a true summer constellation, since it culminates at 8:00 P.M. around July 16 (circle 11.5, Chart I). This statement refers, of course, to the bowl of the Little Dipper; Polaris is almost motionless.

Autumn Constellations

Capricornus, the Goat
Pegasus, the Winged Horse
Aquarius, the Water Carrier or Water Pourer
Piscis Australis, the Southern Fish
Pisces, the Fishes
Cetus, the Whale or Sea Monster
Aries, the Ram
Andromeda, the Chained Lady
Triangulum, the Triangle

CONTINUE the short straight line formed by Altair and the two near-by stars on either side of it downward and you will cross, midway between Altair and the horizon, a large, upside-down triangle with a bent-in base and curving sides— or an upside-down three-cornered hat (à la Napoleon). That hat is Capricornus (pronounced *Kăp-rĭ-kor'nus*), the Goat. The stars of its outlines are faint, yet it is not very difficult to identify Capricornus if you keep in mind that the triangle is rather large, with its stars dispersed over a wide area.

Capricornus is one of the zodiacal constellations; in faintness it is surpassed only by Cancer. The vertex of the triangle culminates at 8:00 P.M. around October 1 (circle 2).

It is interesting to know that a little to the left (east) of Capricornus's triangle is the place where, in 1846, the planet Neptune was observed by Galle, thanks to the tip he received from Leverrier (see p. 17). It takes Neptune 165 years to complete its circuit around the sun, so it will be back at the place of its discovery around 2011; to date it has traveled along the zodiac as far as Virgo.

PEGASUS (pronounced *Peg'a-sus*), the Winged Horse, is the most representative of the autumn constellations, and a very impressive one. The role of Pegasus in Greek mythology is told on p. 58. The Great Square of Pegasus constitutes the major part of the constellation. This square is extensive and striking, all the more so as the area within it is almost empty of lucid stars. You cannot help noticing it in the earlier evening hours from the latter part of September, when it is in the east, until January, when it is in the west.

Except for the Great Square, which is imposing enough, there is nothing in Pegasus of interest for the naked eye. Its brightest star, Alpheratz, which it shares with Andromeda, culminates at 8:00 P.M. around November 21 (circle 3.7).

NOT FAR BELOW the faint star Baham of Pegasus you will find, after some scanning, a small group of four still fainter stars: one symmetrically surrounded by three others so that, however you look, they resemble a Y, though the uppermost of them, the faintest, is often hardly visible. This asterism is the Water Jar of the zodiacal constellation Aquarius (pronounced *A-kwār'ĭ-ŭs*), the Water Carrier or Water Pourer. From this inverted water jar, as the Arabian imagination saw it, the Water Carrier pours water, represented by a shower of very faint stars below the jar, into Fomalhaut ("mouth of the fish"), the principal star of the constellation Piscis Australis (pronounced *Pĭ'sĭs Os-trā'lĭs*), the Southern Fish.

The central star of the Water Jar is almost exactly on the celestial equator; it should be useful in helping you to trace

the equator in the sky. This star culminates at 8:00 P.M. at
the end of October (circle 2.8).

THE FIRST-MAGNITUDE FOMALHAUT is not only the principal
star of Piscis Australis, the Southern Fish, but the only one
of its stars visible in our latitudes without optical aid. This
constellation is always low over the horizon, where all faint
stars are blotted out by the horizon's heavier atmosphere. It
culminates at 8:00 P.M. about November 5 (circle 3.1).

IN THE GENERAL NIEGHBORHOOD of Algenib, the corner star
of the Great Square, are many faint stars, the brightest of
which can be combined into an extensive V. For the beginner
it is difficult to trace these stars, since they are rather close
to the borderline of visibility for the naked eye on an average
clear night, especially when they are not yet high over the
horizon. The inexperienced observer should postpone their
identification until a convenient date and time of culmination of the Square's center, say November 15 at 8:00 P.M.
(circle 3.5). He will then be able to recognize the asterism
Circlet of the zodiacal constellation Pisces (pronounced
Pi'sēz), the Fishes, at the end of the right wing of the V.
From there he should proceed to the left until he reaches the
star Al Risha, the Knot, which is the brightest of all these
stars. From Al Risha the row of stars goes upward, ending
below and to the right of the star Mirach of Andromeda.
  On antiquated starmaps, at the end of each wing of the V
is pictured a fish with a ribbon around its tail. These ribbons
follow the two lines of stars forming the V to Al Risha, where
they are shown tied in a knot. That nonsensical knot has
survived as the common name of Al Risha.

THE LARGEST of all the constellations, Cetus, the Whale or
Sea Monster, is of no interest except for its star Mira, the
Wonderful. Mira was the first variable star (see p. 21) to be
recognized as such. It is a red giant, surpassing our sun in
diameter almost 300 times.

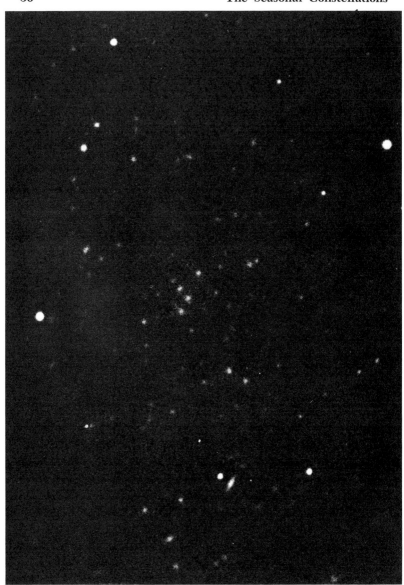

Photograph from the Mt. Wilson and Palomar Observatories

A Cluster of Galaxies in Pisces,
The Limit of the Observable Universe

Mira is located near the head of the Whale, close to circle 5. It varies in magnitude (from about 9 to 3) and also in period (averaging about 330 days); hence it becomes lucid only occasionally. When visible it shines with an orange-colored light.

In 1961 Mira's maximum occurred in June, when, for a few weeks, it was a lucid star in the early morning sky. One can expect that it will again be at maximum in May, 1962, in April, 1963, and so on, although the period of about 11 months can vary considerably.

On Chart II the conventional outlines of Cetus are shown, but all its stars are faint, with the exception of Deneb Kaitos ("the tail of the whale") at the extreme right (west) of the constellation. Deneb Kaitos is of second magnitude (like Polaris) and rather conspicuous because of its lonely situation. It is the nearest bright star in the neighborhood of Fomalhaut, a little higher than, and east of, the latter.

Cetus is the sea monster of the Cassiopeia myth cycle (see p. 58).

NEXT TO PISCES is the constellation Aries (pronounced A'-rǐ-ēz), the Ram. Aries is the first constellation of the zodiac. The point in the sky where the sun crosses the celestial equator in its springtime journey from south to north is called the **vernal equinox.** This occurs about March 21 of each year. Because of a slight, but progressive, shifting of the celestial pole, the "first point of Aries" is now actually in the constellation Pisces. This effect is called **precession** and was the cause of considerable confusion in the history of the calendar.

Aries lies to the left (east) of the Great Square. It is easily identified, as its two brighter stars are rather prominent because of the relative emptiness around them; they just seem to stare at you. The brighter of these two stars is of second magnitude and is called Hamal ("ram" or "sheep"). Hamal culminates at 8:00 P.M. around December 21 (circle 4.7).

LET US RETURN again to the Great Square of Pegasus. Alpheratz, its brightest star, belongs also to another constellation, Andromeda. In the extended direction of a line drawn from Markab to Alpheratz, we see two curved rows of stars, one brighter than the other, but of more or less similar disposition, each row consisting of three stars, and both rows converging into Alpheratz. These two rows of stars, together with Alpheratz, constitute the essential part of Andromeda. Combined with the Great Square, they suggest an immense saucepan, even larger than the Big Dipper.

The stars of Andromeda are of no particular importance, but outside the fainter row of its stars, opposite the star Mirach, lies the famous Great Nebula of Andromeda. It is visible to the naked eye, but only as a very hazy speck, so that to see it one must employ averted vision. It is one of the nearest of all the external galaxies, being about 1.5–2 million light-years distant. It is believed to be a galaxy similar to, but probably somewhat larger than, our Milky Way galaxy.

The photograph of this galaxy on the following page shows that it is tilted toward us. This fortunate circumstance increases its visibility; otherwise, it would probably be completely invisible to the naked eye. Comparing the pictures of the galaxies in Andromeda and Coma Berenices (see p. 70), we see that both resemble our own galaxy as schematically pictured on p. 24. The galaxy in Coma Berenices is seen edgewise by us, while Andromeda's is tilted in our direction.

Until recently the size of the Andromeda galaxy was much underestimated, having been calculated on the basis of photographs. Use of the photoelectric cell, which can detect light where the camera fails, disclosed that the diameter of the galaxy is at least twice the formerly computed figure. The size of this galaxy is now established as somewhat greater than that of the Milky Way.

At the dates and hours of culmination of circle 4 the Andromeda galaxy is almost exactly overhead. Unfortunately, it can be seen only on exceptionally clear nights.

Yerkes Observatory Photograph

THE GREAT NEBULA
IN ANDROMEDA

MIDWAY between Aries and the star Almach of Andromeda lies the inconspicuous and insignificant constellation Triangulum, the Triangle. One claim to fame for this tiny constellation stems from the fact that the Italian astronomer Giuseppe Piazzi discovered Ceres, the first asteroid (see p. 122), in Triangulum on the first day of the nineteenth century. Ceres is only 480 miles in diameter, yet it is the largest of these numerous small planets whose orbits lie between those of Mars and Jupiter.

PEGASUS, Andromeda, Pisces, Cetus, Aries, and Triangulum are not only late-autumn but also early-winter constellations. Since darkness begins before 6:00 P.M. early in winter, these six constellations may be observed through December and January culminating just after nightfall.

Of the circumpolar constellations, Cassiopeia and Cepheus are also easily observed in autumn.

Winter Constellations

Taurus, the Bull
Orion, the Hunter
Canis Major, the Greater Dog
Auriga, the Charioteer

BUT FOR THE COLD, winter is the ideal time for the stargazer. The nights are longest and also clearest, as there is less humidity than in summer, and the most spectacular constellations and stars are on display: Taurus (pronounced *Taw' rŭs*) with the Pleiades, Hyades, and Aldebaran; Orion with Rigel and Betelgeuse; Procyon of the Lesser Dog; Sirius of the Greater Dog; Gemini with Pollux and Castor; and the ubiquitous Cassiopeia.

Strictly speaking, there are no constellations belonging exclusively to winter, because at 6:00 and 7:00 P.M. the late-autumn constellations still culminate, and at very late

Photograph from the Mt. Wilson and Palomar Observatories

THE "CRAB" NEBULA IN TAURUS

Photograph from the Mt. Wilson and Palomar Observatories

THE PLEIADES

hours the early-spring constellations start culminating. For example, Hamal culminates at 8:00 P.M. around December 16 and is therefore a late-autumn star, but it culminates, too, at 7:00 P.M. around January 1 and at 6:00 P.M. around January 16, so it may also be called a winter star. Procyon of Canis Minor culminates at 10:00 P.M. around February 15, and we could call it a winter star, but since it is in transit also at 7:00 P.M. around March 25, we could refer to it equally appropriately as a spring star.

In compliance with our definition of seasonal constellations (see p. 61), we shall consider the winter constellations to be Taurus, the Bull; Orion, the Hunter; Canis Major, the Greater Dog; and Auriga, the Charioteer.

MANY CASUAL OBSERVERS know the lovely cluster of stars called the Pleiades without ever having heard of the constellation Taurus, to which it belongs. The principal star of Taurus is the reddish-hued Aldebaran. In the Greek myth, Aldebaran is the red right eye of the infuriated bull attacking the giant hunter Orion. The two long horns of the bull are represented by two imaginary lines: one from Aldebaran to the star Zeta Tauri, and the other from the end of the right wing of a V formed by the stars of the Hyades (see Chart II) to the star Nath or El Nath. The latter star belongs to two constellations, Taurus and Auriga.

The Pleiades cannot be missed; they rise in October at about 8:00 P.M. to be followed almost exactly one hour later by Aldebaran ("the follower"). The evenings being long in late autumn and winter, this asterism is visible almost all night before it sets in the west.

The average eye sees six stars in the Pleiades, four of them forming a bowl. This subgroup, in conjunction with a fifth star, is sometimes mistakenly taken for the Little Dipper. The lucid stars of the Pleiades are rather faint, being of third magnitude. They coalesce into a haze in the city sky, but elsewhere the total effect of the closely grouped yet distinct stars is very striking.

The Pleiades, like part of the Big Dipper, constitute a galactic cluster. The Pleiades cluster appears small in comparison with that of the Big Dipper, but its distance is greater (about 300 light-years); were it closer, it might look rather like the Big Dipper.

According to Greek mythology, the Pleiades were the seven daughters of the titan Atlas. They were pursued through the forests of Boeotia for five years by the giant Orion before Zeus changed them to doves and then to stars.

Although a winter asterism according to our classification, the Pleiades are already conspicuous in late autumn; as a matter of fact, November is sometimes called the Pleiades month. By November it becomes dark soon enough for the Pleiades to attract attention in the early evening. They remain prominent in the sky all night, not culminating until about 2:00 A.M.

Another galactic cluster in Taurus is the Hyades, forming a V with Aldebaran lying at the end of the letter's left wing. Even though the Hyades are closer to us (about 130 light-years), they are not nearly so conspicuous as the Pleiades; moreover, Aldebaran's brilliance dims them.

The Hyades, too, were daughters of Atlas (half-sisters of the Pleiades) and were transformed into stars by Zeus.

Both the Pleiades cluster and the Hyades cluster are thought to be composed of stars that were born at the same time and under the same circumstances: the Hyades are all old stars, and the Pleiades all young. The fact that the stars in the Hyades are all relatively cool and yellowish in color, and those in the Pleiades are hot and bluish-white, bears out this hypothesis. In case this apparent contradiction disturbs you, namely that both clusters were born at the same time, but now one is old while the other is young, one must consider the lives they have led. Some people are "old" at age 40; other are "young" at 65. The Hyades may also have consumed available fuel quickly; the Pleiades still have a good supply left.

Aldebaran is one of the four Royal Stars and Taurus one

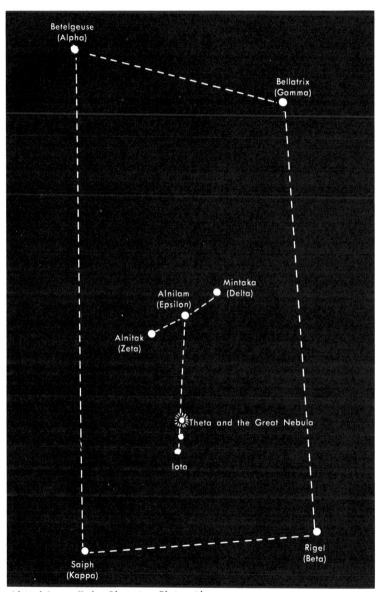

Adapted from a Yerkes Observatory Photograph

THE CONSTELLATION ORION

of the twelve zodiacal constellations. Aldebaran culminates at 8:00 P.M. around January 29 (circle 5.9).

WE NOW COME to the most splendid constellation in the entire northern sky, Orion, the Hunter. In outline Orion is a huge trapezoid with a conspicuous line of stars, suggesting a belt, approximately bisecting it (see p. 95). It is the only constellation that includes *two* first-magnitude stars, Rigel and Betelgeuse.

Orion's aspect is so imposing that in all peoples' legends it represents something great or gigantic. In Greek mythology Orion was a giant hunter of great prowess. His story takes several forms, one of them claiming that he was stung mortally by a scorpion sent by Hera, whose anger he had incurred. In the sky Orion is supposed to be countering the attack of Taurus, the Bull.

The celestial equator touches the top of Orion's Belt. This

Yerkes Observatory Photograph

CENTER OF ORION WITH THE GREAT NEBULA

is mentioned to help the reader trace the equator in the sky. Rigel culminates at 8:00 P.M. around February 8; Betelgeuse, around February 18 (circles 6.3 and 6.6).

The photograph on the preceding page shows Orion's Belt with the hazy patches that make up part of Orion's Sword. The photograph below is a close-up of these patches. They are the Great Nebula in Orion, an immense gas cloud containing enough material for 10,000 suns like ours. This marvel of the winter sky is 1,600 light-years away, about 20 light-

Yerkes Observatory Photograph

CLOSE-UP OF THE GREAT NEBULA IN ORION

Photograph from the Mt. Wilson and Palomar Observatories

THE "HORSEHEAD" NEBULA
IN ORION

years across, and visible as a tiny cloud on very clear nights.
In addition to this luminous cloud there is in Orion a famous dark cloud, the so-called Horsehead Nebula. It is located just below the easternmost of the three bright stars of
Orion's Belt. Looking at a photograph of this cloud of cosmic
dust, one irresistibly gets the impression that its edges are
silver lined by the glow of luminous clouds or myriads of suns
behind it.

ORION is peerless among the constellations, and Sirius is
peerless among the stars. When culminating, Sirius, the Dog
Star, of the constellation Canis Major, the Greater Dog, is
the lowest of the bright stars and the brightest of all of them.
It lies below and to the left (east) of Orion. Sirius is also
one of our nearest neighbors. We have already discussed
several other distinctive features of Sirius and of its dwarf
companion (pp. 9–10). Sirius culminates at 8:00 P.M. around
March 1 (circle 7), but is visible all winter long. The other
stars of Canis Major, though relatively bright, are of no particular interest.

THE LAST CONSTELLATION we shall consider is Auriga, the
Charioteer, the principal star of which, Capella (pronounced
Kă-pel′a), belongs to the circumpolar region. When culminating, the Charioteer is found to the left (east) of Aldebaran
but much higher, at the zenith. Half of Auriga lies in the
Milky Way.
The star El Nath in Auriga is held in common with Taurus,
just as Alpheratz belongs to both Andromeda and Pegasus.
A line drawn through the right wing of the V formed by
the Hyades in Taurus will hit El Nath, which is supposed
to represent the end of the left horn of the charging bull.
Capella is the third brightest star in our latitudes, surpassed only by Sirius and Vega. Sirius is comparatively low
in the sky, whereas Capella is very high, and Vega, being a
summer star, is far distant. Capella, like the sun, is a yellow

star, but it is much larger and more than 150 times more luminous than the sun. At 8:00 P.M. Capella culminates around February 10 (circle 6.3).

Although it is a winter constellation, Auriga is visible at some time during the night throughout the entire year; it is beneath the horizon only four hours a day. When it is culminating, we may look at Auriga facing either south or north; but remember that its outlines will be reversed every time we turn around.

Recapitulation

WITH AURIGA our review of the constellations comes to an end. We have become acquainted with 38 constellations, more than half the number of constellations visible in our latitudes. The others have been omitted because they are inconspicuous, such interesting features as they possess being inaccessible to the naked eye.

TABLE 2

FIRST-MAGNITUDE STARS

Star	Constellation	Apparent Magnitude	Luminosity	Distance in Light-Years
Sun	....	—26.7	1	0.000016
Sirius	Canis Major	—1.42	23.5	8.7
Arcturus	Boötes	—0.06	118	36
Vega	Lyra	0.04	56	27
Capella	Auriga	0.09	155	46
Rigel	Orion	0.15	32,400	650
Procyon	Canis Minor	0.37	7.4	11
Altair	Aquila	0.77	10.7	17
Betelgeuse	Orion	0.78	15,500	660
Aldebaran	Taurus	0.85	170	69
Spica	Virgo	0.96	1,860	155
Antares	Scorpio	0.98	2,240	170
Fomalhaut	Piscis Australis	1.14	14	23
Pollux	Gemini	1.16	32	36
Deneb	Cygnus	1.26	6,170	1,600
Regulus	Leo	1.36	178	85

TABLE 3

SECOND-MAGNITUDE AND FAINTER STARS OF INTEREST

Star(s)	Constellation	Significance
The Pointers .	Big Dipper	They point to the polestar (North Star).
Mizar	Big Dipper	Optical double with Alcor.
Alcor	Big Dipper	Optical double with Mizar. Also called Saidak, "the test." Of fourth magnitude, it was once a test for keenness of vision.
Polaris	Little Dipper	Our present polestar.
Kochab	Little Dipper	Our polestar about 500 B.C.
Thuban	Draco	Our polestar about 3,000 B.C.; will again be our polestar about A.D. 23,000.
Etamin	Draco	Of second magnitude; "the dragon's head."
Delta Cephei .	Cepheus	Prototype of a class of extremely important variables.
Algol	Perseus	The classic eclipsing variable.
Marfak or Algenib ...	Perseus	The brightest star in Perseus.
Denebola	Leo	Of second magnitude; "the lion's tail."
Castor	Gemini	Almost of first magnitude; brighter than Pollux many centuries ago.
Alphard	Hydra	Of second magnitude; "heart of the sea serpent."
Gemma or Alphecca ..	Corona Borealis	"The bright one." Although of second magnitude, its luminosity is 60 times that of the sun.
Ras Algethi ..	Hercules	"The kneeler's head." Only of third magnitude, but actually one of the supergiants.
Ras Alhague ..	Ophiuchus	Of second magnitude; "head of the serpent bearer."
Alpheratz	Pegasus and Andromeda	Common star of both constellations.
Baham	Pegasus	Helpful in locating the Water Jar of Aquarius.
Algenib	Pegasus	Helpful in locating Pisces.
Mira	Cetus	"The wonderful." First variable to be identified.
Deneb Kaitos .	Cetus	Of second magnitude; "the whale's tail."
Hamal	Aries	Of second magnitude; "ram" or "sheep."
Mirach	Andromeda	In its neighborhood lies the Great Nebula of Andromeda.
El Nath	Taurus and Auriga	Common star of both constellations. Tip of the left horn of the bull charging Orion.

Not including the sun, there are 20 stars of first magnitude (not over magnitude 1.5). Fifteen of them are visible from most parts of the United States and have been commented upon in connection with the constellations to which they belong. The table on p. 100 describes these stars in order of their apparent magnitude. It is well to remember that the luminosity and distance values given in the chart may change (and sometimes by a considerable amount) as newer and more precise techniques of measurement are developed.

Not every second-magnitude star visible in our latitudes has been mentioned, as many of them are of no outstanding interest. The more important second-magnitude stars, and also fainter stars of interest, are listed in Table 3, p. 101.

WE CANNOT, offhand, know what constellations of Chart I are higher in the sky than a given constellation of Chart II. We can, of course, find out what the circle of the constellation in question is; looking at the same circle on Chart I then solves the problem. Looking from chart to chart each time to establish such a correspondence is desirable but becomes tedious. On the following page, therefore, you will find a composite of both charts. It represents slightly more than the northern half of the celestial sphere, with Polaris at its center. Around Polaris are the circumpolar constellations, bordered by a circle. This circle represents all the points of the sky through which the zenith of a place of observation at latitude 40° N. passes within 24 hours. On Chart II this circle, unrolled on flat paper, is the zenith line.

The circumpolar constellations always appear almost exactly as they are represented on Chart I, whereas the equatorial constellations on Chart II are identifiable only during the time they are on or near the meridian. The equatorial constellations lie outside the circle on the composite chart. The farther away from the circle they fall, the more distorted their outlines become. We omit the outlines altogether at the periphery, since reproducing unrecognizable shapes would serve no purpose.

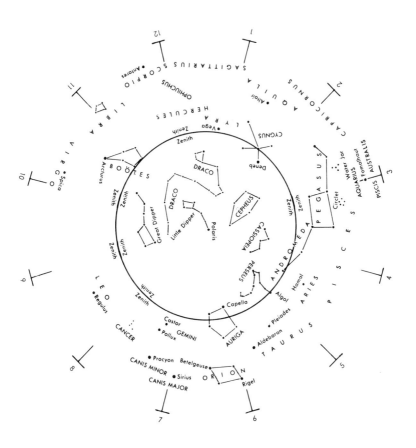

COMPOSITE OF CHARTS I AND II

TABLE 4

THE CONSTELLATIONS

Classical Title	English Title	First-Magnitude Star(s)
Andromeda	The Chained Lady	....
Aquarius (Z)*	The Water Carrier, Pourer	....
Aquila	The Eagle	Altair
Aries (Z)	The Ram	....
Auriga	The Charioteer	Capella
Boötes	The Bear Driver, Plowman	Arcturus
Cancer (Z)	The Crab	....
Canis Major	The Greater Dog	Sirius
Canis Minor	The Lesser Dog	Procyon
Capricornus (Z)	The Goat	....
Cassiopeia	The Queen	....
Cepheus	The King	....
Cetus	The Whale, Sea Monster	....
Coma Berenices	Berenice's Hair	....
Corona Borealis	The Northern Crown	....
Corvus	The Crow	....
Cygnus	The Swan or	Deneb
	The Northern Cross	
Delphinus	The Dolphin	....
Draco	The Dragon	....
Gemini (Z)	The Twins	Pollux
Hercules	Hercules or The Kneeler	....
Hydra	The Sea Serpent	....
Leo (Z)	The Lion	Regulus
Libra (Z)	The Scales	....
Lyra	The Lyre	Vega
Ophiuchus	The Serpent Bearer	....
Orion	Orion or	Rigel and
	The Hunter	Betelgeuse
Pegasus	The Winged Horse	....
Perseus	Perseus	....
Pisces (Z)	The Fishes	....
Piscis Australis	The Southern Fish	Fomalhaut
Sagittarius (Z)	The Archer	....
Scorpio (Z)	The Scorpion	Antares
Taurus (Z)	The Bull	Aldebaran
Triangulum	The Triangle	....
Ursa Major	The Great Bear, including	....
	The Big Dipper	
Ursa Minor	The Little Bear, including	....
	The Little Dipper	
Virgo (Z)	The Virgin	Spica

* (Z) indicates that the constellation is zodiacal.

6

The Planets and the Planetfinder

THE PLANETS are not, astronomically speaking, stars, since they shine with light borrowed from the sun, and stars are properly self-luminous bodies. To the naked eye, however, the visible planets are starlike, and our intention being to familiarize the aspiring stargazer with all the prominent point-sources of light in the night sky, we shall discuss the planets briefly and chart their positions.

There are nine planets, the earth included, but only Venus, Mars, Jupiter, and Saturn are visible to the naked eye. Mercury may be visible once in a lifetime, but it is very near the sun, and never rises very high over the horizon. Haze almost invariably sponges it out entirely; as a matter of fact, many professional astronomers have never observed Mercury. Uranus, Neptune, and Pluto are strictly telescopic.

All planets are seasonal; therefore they are not visible every night. It is important to be in a position to identify them in order to avoid confusing the planets with the genuine stars.

The paths of the planets lie in a belt a little above and below the ecliptic. This narrow belt including the ecliptic and the paths of the planets is called the **zodiac,** whence the name zodiacal constellation arises. Knowing that the elevation of any planet is strictly limited by the zodiac, we need

105

only obtain that planet's calendrical circle to locate it definitely in the sky.

The stars and their circles seem to us to be fixed, without noticeable motion. The planets, on the contrary, move slowly and are now on one circle, then on another. Seen from the sun, the planets move always from west to east (right to left in the Northern Hemisphere). This is their normal motion. Seen from the earth, they normally move also from west to east, but periodically they move from east to west, in **retrograde motion.** Their circles, however, can be determined years in advance and are given in our Planetfinder (see p. 130–132).

Venus, the brightest of the planets, is always brighter than any star in the sky. The magnitude of Sirius is −1.4; that of Venus is −4.3. At its greatest brilliance Venus may be visible even in the daytime, if you know where to look for it and you are in the shade. It is then often mistaken for some extraordinary phenomenon in the sky. Because of its great brilliance Venus is always either an evening star, i.e., the first star to appear in the evening sky, or a morning star, i.e., the last star to disappear in the morning sky.

At their best, Jupiter and Mars are of about the same magnitude, again exceeding the brightness of Sirius. Mars, however, periodically declines considerably in brightness, sinking to the borderline of second magnitude, approximately to the brightness of Polaris. The distinctive feature of Mars is its decidedly reddish hue. Saturn is seldom fainter than first magnitude, and at opposition (see p. 126), it is somewhat brighter than Procyon.

The haze that blots out stars of second and even first magnitude near the horizon will also obscure Saturn and, frequently, Mars. Venus and Jupiter can usually be seen even when they are near the horizon. Of course, in the city sky, observation in the vicinity of the horizon is further hampered.

It is often stated that stars twinkle whereas planets do not. This idea is much overstated as far as the naked eye is concerned. Planets twinkle, too, though much less than stars; the situation depends upon the height of the planet in the sky and the atmospheric conditions. In any event, the difference is not striking enough to serve as a mark of distinction, at least not for the optically unaided beginner. When you look through a telescope the planets do not twinkle but appear as disks of light, while the stars remain points.

Two POSSIBILITIES regarding the planets confront the observer. Either he sees a bright unaccounted-for "star," one not on Chart II, and he wants to know who the stranger is, or he is curious to know which planets will be visible on a particular night.

The first case is the simpler one. Suppose, for example, that late some night in August, 1962, we saw a very bright object in the region of the constellation Taurus, somewhat above and to the left of the star Aldebaran. As there is no bright star on Chart II for such a location, we infer that the bright object was a planet. But which one?

Aldebaran is near circle 6, and by consulting the Planetfinder for August, 1962, we find that Mars, whose circle for the date is 6.2, must have been the planet.

The second case is more complicated. Although we can always find a planet's place in the sky with our Planetfinder, we have still to determine whether it will actually be visible on a particular evening. This probem can be solved by comparing the planet's circle with that of the sun for the same day.

If the planet's circle is numerically greater than the sun's, the planet lags behind the sun in its diurnal movement from east to west and therefore sets *later* than the sun and may be visible after sunset. If its circle is less than the sun's, it moves ahead of the sun, sets *before* sunset, and will be invisible that evening; but as it will also rise before sunrise the next morning, it may be visible then. As the time interval between any circle C and $C + 1$ or $C - 1$ is two hours, we can determine how many hours later than the sun the planet will set or how many hours earlier than the sun the planet will rise.

This information, however, is not quite enough, because

after sunset and before sunrise the two periods of twilight further hem in the hours of complete darkness. Thus we must consider, in addition to the planet's circle for the day, the hours of sunset and sunrise and of the end of evening twilight and the beginning of morning twilight. These times are included in the table on p. 125.

PROBABLY THE BEST WAY to demonstrate the use of the Planetfinder is to consider the events for a particular evening, say November 1, 1962. (The year does not matter in the case of the sun; however, it does for the planets, since they are always moving with respect to both the stars and the sun.)

For this date, we find from Table 6 on p. 125 the following data for the sun: the sun, circle 11, sets at 4:58 P.M.; evening twilight ends at 6:30 P.M.; morning twilight begins at 4:56 A.M.; and the sun rises at 6:28 A.M. Therefore the sky is fully dark from 6:30 P.M., November 1, to 4:56 A.M., November 2, a period of 10 hours, 26 minutes.

For Venus: At noon, November 1, 1962, we find from the Planetfinder (pp. 130–132) that Venus's circle is 11.6, the sun's being 11.0. The sun is on the meridian at noon and is thus culminating. The difference between Venus's circle and that of the sun is 0.6 circle interval, and since each circle interval represents a time-lapse of 2 hours, there is a time-difference of 1.2 hours, or 1 hour, 12 minutes. Since Venus's circle (11.6) is numerically greater than the sun's (11.0) we know that Venus crosses the meridian 1 hour and 12 minutes *after* the sun. It also rises and sets after the sun.

Now circle 11.6 is on the meridian at noon on November 19 together with the then culminating sun. (Recall that circle 11.0 stands for November and that 0.6 circle interval means 0.6 × 30 days plus 1 day, or 19 days.) Interpolating from Table 6 we find that for November 19 the sun rises at 6:48 A.M. and sets at 4:44 P.M. (The rising time for November 1 is 6:28 A.M.; for December 1 it is 7:01 A.M. November 19 is about ⅗ of a month beyond November 1, so we add ⅗ of the time-difference of 33 minutes, or 20 minutes, to 6:28 A.M., obtaining 6:48 A.M. The setting time of 4:44 P.M. is obtained in the same way.)

At noon on November 1 circle 11.6 with Venus on it is not yet on the meridian (the sun is, of course); it follows 1 hour, 12 minutes after the sun. Hence on November 1 Venus sets 1 hour, 12 minutes after the sun sets—1:12 plus 4:44, or at 5:56 P.M. Venus rises 1 hour, 12 minutes after the sun rises— 1:12 plus 6:48, or at 8:00 A.M.

Since evening twilight ends at 6:30 P.M. it is quite likely that Venus, our brightest planet, would be visible just above the western horizon. It would be near the ecliptic, close to the star Antares, in the constellation Scorpio. Venus is always close to the sun, rarely being more than 3 hours away from the sun's setting and rising times. Since morning twilight begins at 4:56 A.M. and Venus rises at 8:00 A.M., there would not be much likelihood of observing Venus as a morning star.

For Mars: At noon, November 1, 1962, Mars is at circle 8.0 and the sun is at circle 11.0 and is culminating. Their difference is 3.0 circle intervals, corresponding to a time-difference of 6 hours. Since the circle for Mars is numerically less than that of the sun, Mars is *ahead* of the sun by 6 hours.

Now circle 8.0 is on the meridian at noon on August 1 with the then culminating sun. On that date the sun rises at 4:56 A.M. and sets at 7:16 P.M. Hence we know that Mars rises at 10:56 P.M. the night before and sets at 1:16 P.M.

Since Mars sets before the sun, it would not be observable as an evening star. But morning twilight begins at 4:56 A.M. on November 1, so Mars would be visible as a morning star for fully 6 hours. It would be practically on the ecliptic, in the southeast about halfway between the stars Pollux and Regulus, in the constellation Cancer.

For Jupiter: At noon, November 1, 1962, Jupiter's circle is 2.7; the sun is at circle 11.0 and is culminating. Their difference is 8.3 circle intervals, corresponding to a time-difference of 16.6 hours, or 16 hours, 36 minutes. Since Jupiter's circle is numerically smaller than the sun's, Jupiter is *ahead* of the

sun by 16 hours, 36 minutes. (This can also be construed as
Jupiter's being *behind* the sun by 7 hours, 24 minutes. Calculations are sometimes easier from this viewpoint.)

Now circle 2.7 is on the meridian at noon on February 22
with the then culminating sun, which rises at 6:45 A.M. and
sets at 5:41 P.M. Hence we know that Jupiter rises at 2:09
P.M. and sets at 1:05 A.M., both on October 31.

Since Jupiter sets before the onset of morning twilight, it
would not be observable as a morning star, but it would be
seen as a brilliant evening star. It would be well up in the
southeast sky at sunset, in the constellation Aquarius, almost
directly above Fomalhaut.

For Saturn: At noon, November 1, 1962, Saturn's circle is
1.8; the sun is at circle 11.0 and is culminating. Their difference is 9.2 circle intervals, corresponding to a time-difference
of 18.4 hours, or 18 hours, 24 minutes. Since Saturn's circle
is numerically smaller than the sun's, Saturn is *ahead* of the
sun by 18 hours, 24 minutes (or *behind* the sun by 5 hours,
36 minutes).

Now circle 1.8 is on the meridian at noon on January 25
with the then culminating sun, which rises at 7:12 A.M. and
sets at 5:12 P.M. Hence we know that Saturn rises at 12:48
P.M. and sets at 10:48 P.M. Saturn would be observable, therefore, just about on the meridian at sunset, in the constellation
Capricornus. It would be readily identifiable, being the only
bright object in the area.

CALCULATIONS similar to those just given for the four lucid
planets, in which the times are stated to the minute, involve
somewhat unwarranted refinements from the point of view
of the naked-eye observer. We are not, in practical stargazing, dealing with sky conditions that are ideal; haze at the
horizon is usually very bothersome and tends to make star-
setting times seem earlier than expected, and rising times
later. Exactitude, therefore, is unnecessary. In addition, two
factors work against a high degree of precision in our computations. First, a planet is, more often than not, only ap-

proximately on the ecliptic (since the planetary orbits make small angles with the ecliptic plane), but this involves discrepancies of only a few minutes. Second, our circles are computed only to one decimal place; the values 11.6, 0.6, and 1.2 listed for Venus are more precisely 11.63, 0.63, and 1.27. In most cases these differences are negligible. In the worst combination of circumstances, our computed times for the planets are not apt to be off by more than 25 minutes, an unimportant error for our purposes.

A STAR exactly on the celestial equator rises exactly six hours before culmination and sets exactly six hours after culmination. Stars higher than the equator rise earlier and set later, remaining longer in the sky. Conversely, stars below the equator rise later and set earlier. If you know the times of rising and setting for some particular star, you can count upon its performing consistently for years to come. In fact, we ultimately measure our time by the stars rather than by the sun, the apparent movement of which is rather erratic. For purposes of convenient living, however, we do not use star time, or **sidereal time** but have devised a scheme known as **mean solar time,** which is based on a fictitious sun whose apparent motion is perfectly uniform.

The planets are not nearly so dependable as the stars. They are always somewhere near the ecliptic, to be sure, but they move with very inconstant motions in their elliptical orbits. Since the earth is also a planet, with its own irregular motion, and since we are viewing the whole sky from a moving observation point, we can expect the planets to show most changeable positions from night to night.

Since the ecliptic is sometimes higher, sometimes lower, than the celestial equator (which is really an extension of the earth's own equator), it follows that the planets will be found at various heights above the southern horizon at culmination. It happens that, for the evening hours, the ecliptic is higher in winter than in summer. Thus a planet is higher in winter than in summer, rising earlier and setting later. The best time of the year for viewing the planets, therefore, is winter.

Although we can make a starmap that will remain perfectly usable for thousands of years, we can make no such map for the planets. The complex motions of the planets, even in one day, would render our map useless. Hence we have devised the Planetfinder, by means of which we can predict the paths of the planets for any specified night.

It may appear strange that Saturn's circles on the Planetfinder tables change very slowly, whereas those of Venus, for example, change very rapidly. We need only remember that the planets obey the laws of classical mechanics in revolving around the sun. The nearer the sun a planet is, the harder the sun pulls on it. In order not to be pulled into the sun, the nearer planets must orbit with greater velocities. For this reason the rate of motion of Mercury, the nearest planet to the sun, is far greater than that of Pluto, the farthest. Pluto's orbit is about 100 times longer than Mercury's, but its period of revolution is not 100 but 1,000 times that of Mercury. Pluto travels at one-tenth the speed of Mercury, requiring almost two and one-half centuries to circle the sun, a feat accomplished by Mercury in three months. When comparing Saturn with Venus on the Planetfinder, therefore, we must remember that in the time required by Saturn to circle the sun once, Venus makes almost 50 circuits.

What exactly are we looking at when we locate a planet in the night sky: another earth? Not at all. Differences in distance from the sun and planetary atmosphere create appreciable differences in the physical features of the planets.

MERCURY is not very much larger than our moon; its diameter is only 3,000 miles. It has no satellites. Because of its proximity to the sun, the extremes of temperature must be immense, even if Mercury rotates. It is believed, however, that Mercury always turns the same side toward the sun, just as the same side of the moon always faces the earth. If this is so, its sunlit part must have a temperature exceeding 600° F.,

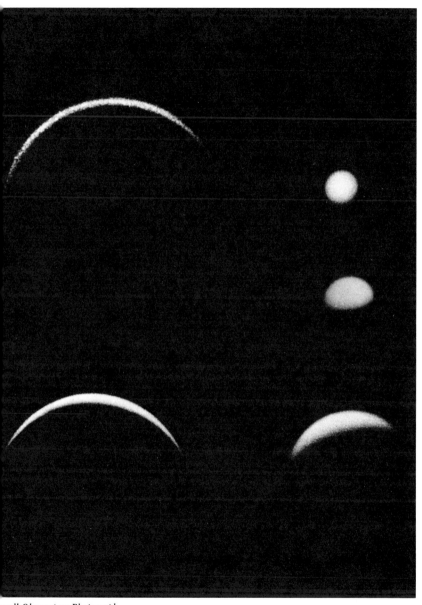

VENUS AT
DIFFERENT PHASES

whereas the temperature of the opposite side must approach —460° F., absolute zero. There is little or no atmosphere on Mercury which could temper these extremes. Neither the telescope nor the camera furnishes enough details to give us an idea of the nature of the surface of Mercury.

VENUS is almost the same size as the earth and is often called our sister planet. Its appearance through the telescope (p. 113) is almost spotlessly white, and although there are no markings that might assist the astronomer in accurately determining its period of rotation, there is evidence that it rotates on its axis in a period of about one month.

The absence of markings and the color of Venus are ascribed to the existence of dense, white, carbon dioxide clouds enveloping the planet. This cloud layer has frustrated all attempts to gain information about the surface features of Venus.

Some astronomers state that neither animal nor plant life can exist on Venus, and this seems to be true in the light of present-day knowledge. Still, we may be discounting the implications of an atmosphere quite different from ours. A few decades ago it was accepted as beyond any doubt that the temperature of the earth's atmosphere gradually and uninterruptedly decreases as the distance from the earth's surface increases, until absolute zero is reached. We now know that the terrestrial atmosphere consists of alternating very hot and very cold layers. We are absolutely ignorant of what surprises an atmosphere like that of Venus may hold for us. Nevertheless, we can, at least, measure the temperature of Venus's cloud cover. Astronomers are not universally agreed upon these measurements, but it does seem that the sunlit clouds are the same temperature as the clouds over the dark side.

There are those who admit the possibility of intelligent life on Venus. They go so far as to pity the poor Venusians, who must live under an opaque roof of clouds, never to see the beauties of the sky. But who knows? Are we terrestrials not already using electronic telescopes to penetrate areas of the heavens impenetrable to optical telescopes? Why should the Venusians, if they exist, be inferior to us in scientific achievement?

THE DIAMETER OF MARS is only a little more than half that of the earth, and its mass is only about one-tenth ours. Whereas Mercury and Venus hold very little of interest for the telescope, Mars is a horn of plenty for the telescopic observer's fancy. There is an abundance of markings, stirring one's imagination as well as assisting the astronomer in determining the planet's characteristics.

Mars is similar to the earth in several respects. It rotates on its axis, the period of its rotation being only one-half hour longer than that of the earth. The Martian year also has its four seasons. Because Mars completes one circuit around the sun in somewhat less than two earth-years (687 earth-days), the Martian seasons are about twice as long as ours.

The most striking features of Mars are the white caps that cover its poles. These caps increase in size during the Martian winter and decrease in summer, naturally suggesting snow. The rest of the surface of Mars consists of reddish and gray-green patches, the colors of which change in intensity with the seasons, suggesting that the gray-green areas are covered with some kind of vegetation.

A sensation was created in 1877 when the Italian astronomer G. V. Schiaparelli declared that the surface of Mars is covered with a network of very fine lines; he called these lines *canali*, which may be translated either "channels" (probably Schiaparelli's intention) or "canals" (the generally circulated translation). Imaginative people immediately attributed these canals to intelligent beings on Mars. Many astronomers were unable to see the canals, however, so for years an acrimonious war was waged between the pros and the cons. By now passions have calmed; it is conceded that these canals may exist, but it is held unlikely.

The same must be said with regard to life on Mars. If plant or animal life does exist, it must be very different from ours.

The Martian atmosphere, although in some respects similar to ours, is exceedingly tenuous and oxygen-poor, and the climate is extremely severe in comparison with ours.

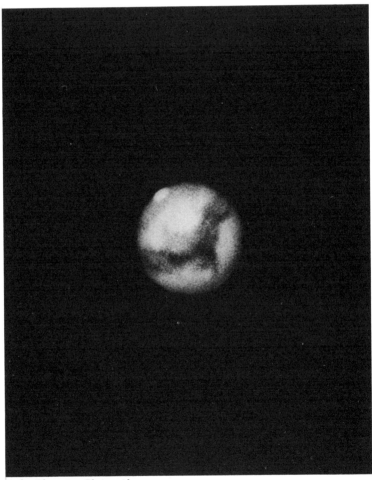

Yerkes Observatory Photograph

MARS

It may seem strange that there persists a dispute about canals on Mars after telescopes capable of penetrating millions and even billions of light-years into space have been built. Unfortunately, the earth's atmosphere places a practical limit on the useful magnifying power of a telescope. The air is never absolutely homogeneous. Ever-present air currents of different densities cause distortions in the telescopic image; the greater the magnification, the greater the distortions. The real advantage of the larger telescopes lies in their light-gathering capacity, especially in conjunction with the camera.

Mars has two tiny satellites—so tiny that their diameters cannot be measured but only estimated at from five to ten miles. The inner, larger satellite is called Phobos and the outer satellite Deimos ("Fear" and "Panic" in Greek), fitting companions for Mars, the god of war. They are unusually interesting, both from an astronomical and a literary standpoint.

Phobos revolves so rapidly around Mars that it completes more than three circuits in one Martian day. Our moon takes 29 times as long to get around the earth as the earth takes to spin once on its axis. Our moon's revolution and the earth's rotation are both from west to east, so every day the moon rises in the east and sets in the west, as the stars do. Phobos, on the other hand, is in such a great hurry that it "overtakes" the hypothetical Martian observer two times a Martian day. Thus, although both Mars and Phobos move in the same direction, from west to east, Phobos rises in the *west* and sets in the *east*. Phobos is unique in the solar system in this respect.

In 1726 Jonathan Swift published his satirical masterpiece *Gulliver's Travels*. The astronomers of the floating island Laputa inform Gulliver that they have discovered two satellites of Mars. The inner satellite, they announce, revolves once about the parent planet in ten hours, the outer satellite in somewhat more than twenty. It is astounding enough that our modern figures for the periods of revolution of Phobos and Deimos are seven and one-half hours and thirty hours, but the very *existence* of the two satellites was not confirmed until 1877.

JUPITER is the giant among the planets. Its diameter is about 11 times that of the earth, and its volume more than 1,300 times as great. Jupiter's mass, however, is only 318 times that of the earth, because its density is but one-fourth that of our planet. It seems—we have no way as yet of being certain —that Jupiter's core is of solid hydrogen and that it is surrounded by a thick layer of solidly frozen ammonia. Around the frozen ammonia, finally, is an atmosphere of hydrogen and methane (marsh gas), in which float clouds of icy ammonia crystals. The temperature of the cloud layer is about $-220°$ F.

Although it is 11 times as large in diameter as the earth, Jupiter completes one rotation in about 10 hours, compared with the earth's 24 hours. Because of this rapid rotation Jupiter bulges at the equator to a much greater extent than does the earth, so that its disk appears noticeably flattened. Jupiter's surface features, beautiful through a telescope, also include many-colored bands and the famous Great Red Spot, of unknown origin.

Jupiter has 12 satellites. Thanks to four of them, Roemer was able to show that light is not propagated instantaneously.

SATURN is the outermost of the lucid planets. In size it is not much inferior to Jupiter, its diameter being nine times that of the earth. Its mass is less than one-third of Jupiter's, making Saturn the least dense of all the planets; it is actually less dense than water. Consequently, any solid core could not be very large. Methane is more prominent in Saturn's atmosphere than in Jupiter's; otherwise the atmospheres of the two planets are quite similar. Saturn is colder and flatter at the poles than Jupiter.

The remarkable feature of Saturn, of course, is its system of concentric rings. The rings are probably composed of the debris of a shattered satellite. Between the two main rings is a gap known as Cassini's division, after the Italian astronomer Giovanni Cassini (1625–1712), who discovered it. There is a third, inner ring, which is almost transparent. Unfortunately, the rings are not visible to the naked eye.

JUPITER AT DIFFERENT STAGES IN ITS ROTATION

Note the shadow of a satellite in the top photograph, and both the satellite and its shadow in the bottom photograph.

Yerkes Observatory Photograph

SATURN

The ring system is wide but exceedingly thin—so thin that it disappears when it is turned edgewise to us. In this position Saturn is least bright. When the rings are tilted toward us, Saturn increases in brightness several times, and at its best it is even brighter than Vega (but still fainter than Sirius). Saturn has nine satellites in addition to the ring system.

BEYOND the information in the table below, not very much can be said about the remaining three planets, Uranus, Neptune, and Pluto. Uranus and Neptune are similar in many respects to Jupiter and Saturn; of course, they are commensurately colder. Interestingly, the position of Neptune was derived mathematically before it was actually observed. Uranus has five known satellites, Neptune two.

Pluto is so remote that little is known about it. Like Neptune, Pluto was "predicted" before it was seen, but the interval between the prediction and the observation was not a few hours as was the case with Neptune but many years, so difficult is Pluto to locate. Pluto may once have been a satellite of Neptune that somehow broke free of the parent planet.

TABLE 5

CHARACTERISTICS OF THE SUN, MOON, AND PLANETS

	DIAMETER		VOLUME	DENSITY	MASS	DISTANCE FROM SUN	
	Miles	Earth = 1	Earth = 1	Water = 1	Earth = 1	Million Miles	Astronomical Units[1]
Sun	864,000	109	1,300,000	1.4	332,000	....	....
Moon ...	2,160	0.27	0.02	3.3	0.012	93	1.0
Mercury .	3,000	0.38	0.055	5.4	0.056	36	0.4
Venus ...	7,600	0.96	0.88	4.9	0.80	67	0.7
Earth ...	7,920	1.00	1.00	5.5	1.00	93	1.0
Mars	4,200	0.53	0.15	4.0	0.11	142	1.5
Jupiter ..	86,800	10.9	1,325	1.3	318	483	5.2
Saturn ..	71,500	9.0	730	0.7	95	886	9.5
Uranus ..	29,400	3.7	50	1.6	15	1,780	19
Neptune .	28,000	3.5	43	2.5	17	2,790	30
Pluto [2] ..	7,600	0.96	0.88	5.8	0.93	3,670	40

[1] One astronomical unit equals the distance from the earth to the sun, about 93 million miles.

[2] The data for Pluto are somewhat uncertain.

THE FOUR LUCID PLANETS are not the only members of the

sun's family that we can see. A continuous swarm of **meteors** bombards the earth daily. Most of them are reduced to dust by the atmosphere, but a few exceptionally large specimens reach the earth's surface, becoming **meteorites.** Atmospheric friction causes meteors to become incandescent. The larger incandescent meteors are visible for a few seconds and are popularly called shooting or falling stars.

Between the orbits of Mars and Jupiter, tiny planets called **asteroids** revolve around the sun. The largest of them, Ceres, is 480 miles in diameter, and the brightest of them, Vesta, can be seen with the naked eye (but only under extremely favorable circumstances). There are thousands of telescopic asteroids.

Among the more puzzling of the objects that accompany the sun in its interstellar journey are the **comets.** They are, with rare exceptions, telescopic and therefore not within the scope of this book. Meteors may be the remnants of comets that have broken up.

We have paid little attention to the second brightest object in the heavens precisely because of its prominence; the moon is not difficult to locate. Our one natural satellite is 239,000 miles away and one-fourth the diameter of the earth. It is the largest satellite in relation to the parent planet in the solar system, although in absolute terms two of Jupiter's satellites and one of Saturn's are larger than the moon.

Because the moon rotates once in exactly the same period of time in which it revolves once around the earth, it always presents the same face to us. Depending on how much of the side of the moon lighted by the sun is visible to us, we see no moon at all, a crescent, a half moon, a gibbous moon, or a full moon. The familiar radiance and surface markings of the moon have been sung by poets from time immemorial.

THE SUN, the nine planets with their satellites, the mysterious wandering comets, the thousands of asteroids, and billions of meteors make up the solar system. In asking how the solar system came to be, we should remind ourselves of the scale of our inquiry. We on earth naturally feel that the history of the sun and its family must be almost inconceivably awe-inspiring. Awe-inspiring it certainly is, but remember that the sun is one insignificant star among billions in the Milky Way galaxy, revolving around the galactic center once every 200 million years, and that our galaxy is one among billions of galaxies, each of which seemingly moving away from every other at tremendous speeds. We are really, it appears, dealing in very local history when we ask: How did the solar system originate?

The beginnings of the solar system are still shrouded in mystery. Recent findings in geology, physics, and chemistry indicate a probable age of some eight billion years. But what happened eight billion years ago?

In 1796 Laplace suggested that everything started with an enormous, flat, rotating mass of gas. By a process of contracting and throwing off rings of gas, each of which in turn later condensed into a planet with its satellites, the solar system was born. Laplace's view was very appealing in the light of what was then known and held the field for about a century.

With increasing knowledge there came the need for a more satisfactory hypothesis. In the early part of this century advocates of the dynamical-encounter theory suggested that some other star once brushed near our own sun and by its gigantic attraction pulled two arms of hot gases from the sun. These arms later disintegrated and cooled into the planets and satellites. This hypothesis had the merit of explaining the occurrence of planets that come in pairs, like Jupiter and Saturn. It, too, fell by the wayside because it failed to account for all the facts.

A more recent theory, proposed by Whipple, starts with a large cloud of dust that by gravitational attraction condenses into a large central star, leaving behind fringe areas that had earlier formed into planets (implying that the planets are older than the sun). Kuiper begins with a central mass of stuff that ultimately is to become the sun, surrounded by a large disklike cloud that is slowly rotating and eventually becomes the planets and their attendants. Other astronomers begin with the assumption that the sun was once one member of a binary system and consider the planets to have resulted from the explosion of the sun's companion star.

It is abundantly clear that we must have much more information than is now at hand before we can accept any theory concerning the formation of the solar system. This information can be gathered only by sustained and carefully planned study of the problems involved.

The most interesting fact about the solar system for many of us is that we are in it—in other words, that it supports intelligent life. Is it possible that elsewhere in space there may be other stars like our sun, with similar solar systems? Purely as a matter of mathematical probability, it *is* likely that millions of such systems do exist, but unfortunately we shall never be able to see them with even the best present and proposed telescopes. Even if the closest star (Proxima Centauri in the southern celestial hemisphere, some 4 light-years away) had a planet as large as Jupiter revolving around it, we could not resolve the planet with our best equipment. And would any of these other planets support life? Again, the odds are in favor of it. Perhaps a future astronaut will encounter extraterrestrial life and literally new worlds will open up to man.

The Planetfinder

FOR THE DETERMINATION of a planet's visibility we have to know, in addition to the sun's circle, the times of sunset and sunrise, and the times of the end of evening twilight and the beginning of morning twilight. These data are given in Table 6 for the first day of every month.

For intermediate dates, intermediate values are to be derived by interpolation. All times are standard time at the place of observation.

The sun's circles are numbered in accordance with their calendrical order. This is the basis of our method.

TABLE 6

Date	Circle	Sunset	End of Evening Twilight	Start of Morning Twilight	Sunrise
Jan. 1	1	4:45	6:22	5:45	7:22
Feb. 1	2	5:19	6:51	5:37	7:09
Mar. 1	3	5:51	7:21	5:05	6:35
Apr. 1	4	6:25	7:57	4:13	5:46
May 1	5	6:53	8:37	3:18	5:02
June 1	6	7:22	9:22	2:35	4:34
July 1	7	7:33	9:35	2:32	4:35
Aug. 1	8	7:16	9:03	3:06	4:56
Sept. 1	9	6:33	8:08	3:55	5:26
Oct. 1	10	5:45	7:13	4:25	5:55
Nov. 1	11	4:58	6:30	4:56	6:28
Dec. 1	12	4:35	6:15	5:26	7:01

For more precise determinations of time it may be desired to apply the following corrections to the values given in Table 6. These corrections derive from the fact that the cities selected are not located at the center of their respective standard time zones.

For visual purposes such as we contemplate most of these corrections are hardly necessary.

TABLE 7

City	Correction	City	Correction
Baltimore	add 6 min.	Milwaukee	deduct 9 min.
Boston	deduct 16 min.	New York	deduct 4 min.
Buffalo	add 15 min.	Philadelphia	add 1 min.
Chicago	deduct 10 min.	St. Louis	add 1 min.
Cincinnati	add 38 min.	San Francisco ..	add 10 min.
Cleveland	add 26 min.	Washington	add 8 min.
Denver	add 0 min.	Montreal	deduct 6 min.
Detroit	add 32 min.	Toronto	add 18 min.
Indianapolis	deduct 15 min.	Ottawa	add 3 min.
Kansas City	add 18 min.	Vancouver	add 12 min.
Los Angeles	deduct 7 min.	Halifax	add 14 min.

In the following tables you will find the circles for the sun and for the planets Venus, Mars, Jupiter, and Saturn at noon, standard time, for the first of every month through 1970. For intermediate dates, simply determine proportionately intermediate values. Although this procedure is not absolutely accurate, the inaccuracies involved are negligible for our purposes.

A planet's normal motion in the sky is from west to east. In the Northern Hemisphere, where we live, this means that the planets travel from right to left (remember that we are facing south). Periodically a planet appears to move from east to west (left to right); this is called **retrograde motion** (as noted on p. 106 above) to distinguish it from **normal** or **direct motion.** Retrograde motion is a consequence of the ever-changing relative positions in space of the earth and the planets.

Normal motions are shown by increasing circle values as time goes by, retrograde motions by decreasing values.

If a planet's circle is of greater value than the sun's, then the planet can be an evening star; if less, a morning star.

When the values of a planet's circle and the sun's circle are the same, the planet is said to be in **conjunction** with the sun. It then rises and sets with the sun and will not be visible. As soon as the two circle values begin to differ, the times of setting and rising will also begin to differ. When this difference is equal to or longer than the duration of twilight, the planet becomes visible; it remains visible longer and longer as the difference increases.

A glance at Table 6 shows that the duration of twilight is from 1½ hours in winter to 2 hours in summer. The equivalents on our charts are ¾ to 1 circle interval. Hence, a difference of ¾ to 1 between a planet's circle and the sun's circle is an indication that the planet may be visible. Finally, when the difference between the two circles becomes 6, the planet and the sun will be 12 hours apart. When the sun sets, the planet rises, and vice versa. The planet and the sun are then said to be in **opposition.** Opposition is analogous to the full-moon relationship; the alignment of the bodies is planet —— earth —— sun.

Oppositions are of particular importance in the case of Mars, as its brightness changes enormously depending upon its distance from us. Mars is half again as far from the sun as we are; the earth is 1 astronomical unit (93 million miles) from the sun, Mars 1.5 units. At opposition the alignment is

Mars —— earth —— sun.

The distance between Mars and the earth is therefore 1.5 − 1, or 0.5 astronomical unit. At conjunction the alignment is

earth —— sun —— Mars.

The distance between Mars and the earth is then 1 + 1.5, or 2.5 astronomical units, five times the distance at opposition. Mars is 20 times brighter at opposition than at conjunction.

TABLE 8

OPPOSITION OF MARS

Year	Date	Circle of the Sun	Circle of Mars
1963........	Feb. 4	2.2	8.2
1965........	Mar. 9	3.4	9.4
1967........	Apr. 15	4.5	10.5
1969........	May 31	6.0	12.0

Since the earth's orbit is larger than that of Venus, an alignment such as

Venus —— earth —— sun

(opposition) is impossible. But Venus does have two different conjunctions: the alignment

earth —— Venus —— sun,

called an **inferior conjunction;** and the alignment

earth —— sun —— Venus,

called a **superior conjunction.** The superior conjunction of

Venus is sometimes referred to simply as its conjunction. Venus is 0.7 astronomical unit from the sun. It is 1 — 0.7, or 0.3, astronomical unit from the earth when it is at inferior conjunction and 1 + 0.7, or 1.7, astronomical units away when at superior conjunction.

Unlike the case of Mars, the effect of distance on the brightness of Venus is almost negligible. Venus at inferior conjunction is in a position analogous to that of the new moon and is therefore not visible. In a few days it rapidly regains its brilliance as a waxing crescent, long and thin. At superior conjunction the full disk is visible, but Venus is much farther away. The net effect is that, at every position except inferior conjunction, Venus shines steadily bright, surpassed in brilliance only by the moon and the sun.

Since the orbit of Venus is only about seven-tenths as large as the earth's, Venus can never appear at an angular distance of more than 48 degrees from the sun's position in the sky. It shows a **greatest elongation** to the east of the sun when it is an evening star, and to the west of the sun when it is a morning star. Venus is at its brightest about 36 days before and after inferior conjunction.

TABLE 9

CONJUNCTIONS AND GREATEST ELONGATIONS OF VENUS

YEAR	CONJUNCTIONS		GREATEST ELONGATIONS	
	Superior	Inferior	East (Evening Star)	West (Morning Star)
1962......	Jan. 27	Nov. 12	Sept. 3	....
1963......	Aug. 29	....	......	Jan. 23
1964......	......	June 19	Apr. 10	Aug. 29
1965......	Apr. 12	....	Nov. 15	....
1966......	Nov. 9	Jan. 26	......	Apr. 6
1967......	......	Aug. 30	June 21	Nov. 9
1968......	June 20	....	......	....
1969......	......	Apr. 8	Jan. 25	June 17
1970......	Jan. 24	Nov. 10	Sept. 1	......

Jupiter and Saturn also vary in brightness depending upon

conjunction or opposition, but the variations are not so dramatic as those of Mars. Since the distance from the sun to Jupiter is 5.2 astronomical units, Jupiter is 4.2 units from us at its nearest and 6.2 units at its farthest. Saturn is 9.5 astronomical units from the sun; hence it varies in its distance from the earth from 8.5 to 10.5 units. For Mars a difference of 2 astronomical units, between 0.5 and 2.5 units, means that the planet is five times as far away from us at conjunction as at opposition; the same difference of 2 astronomical units in the case of Saturn places it only $\frac{5}{4}$ as far from us at conjunction as at opposition.

TABLE 10

OPPOSITION OF JUPITER AND SATURN

Year	Jupiter	Saturn
1962............	Aug. 31	July 31
1963............	Oct. 8	Aug. 13
1964............	Nov. 13	Aug. 24
1965............	Dec. 18	Sept. 6
1966............	......	Sept. 19
1967............	Jan. 21	Oct. 2
1968............	Feb. 20	Oct. 14
1969............	Mar. 21	Oct. 28
1970............	Apr. 21	Nov. 11

The Planetfinder (p. 130–132) thus tells the positions of the four lucid planets on any evening at any hour, whether they are visible, when they rise and set, and how bright they may be expected to appear. Only our constant reference to the sun at noon makes the provision of this information in a simple table possible.

TABLE 11

THE PLANETFINDER

Date	Sun	Venus	Mars	Jupiter	Saturn
1962 Jan. 1 ...	1	12.8	12.9	2.0	1.6
Feb. 1 ...	2	2.0	1.7	2.2	1.7
Mar. 1 ...	3	3.3	2.3	2.2	1.8
Apr. 1 ...	4	4.5	3.2	2.2	1.9
May 1 ...	5	5.8	4.6	2.2	1.9
June 1 ...	6	7.1	4.8	2.3	2.0
July 1 ...	7	8.2	5.5	2.4	1.9
Aug. 1 ...	8	9.5	6.2	2.6	1.9
Sept. 1 ...	9	10.6	6.9	2.9	1.8
Oct. 1 ...	10	11.4	7.5	2.8	1.8
Nov. 1 ...	11	11.6	8.0	2.7	1.8
Dec. 1 ...	12	11.2	8.4	2.8	1.8
1963 Jan. 1 ...	1	11.6	8.6	3.0	1.9
Feb. 1 ...	2	12.6	8.3	3.2	2.0
Mar. 1 ...	3	1.6	7.9	3.4	2.1
Apr. 1 ...	4	2.7	7.9	3.7	2.2
May 1 ...	5	4.0	8.3	3.9	2.3
June 1 ...	6	5.2	8.7	4.1	2.4
July 1 ...	7	6.4	9.3	4.2	2.3
Aug. 1 ...	8	7.8	9.9	4.3	2.3
Sept. 1 ...	9	9.0	10.5	4.3	2.2
Oct. 1 ...	10	10.3	11.2	4.3	2.2
Nov. 1 ...	11	11.5	11.9	4.0	2.2
Dec. 1 ...	12	12.7	12.7	4.0	2.2
1964 Jan. 1 ...	1	2.0	1.4	4.0	2.3
Feb. 1 ...	2	3.3	2.2	4.2	2.4
Mar. 1 ...	3	4.4	2.9	4.3	2.5
Apr. 1 ...	4	5.6	3.8	4.3	2.6
May 1 ...	5	6.6	4.5	4.8	2.7
June 1 ...	6	7.0	5.3	5.1	2.8
July 1 ...	7	6.4	6.0	5.3	2.8
Aug. 1 ...	8	6.5	6.7	5.4	2.7
Sept. 1 ...	9	7.5	7.3	5.5	2.6
Oct. 1 ...	10	8.6	8.0	5.5	2.6
Nov. 1 ...	11	9.8	8.7	5.2	2.6
Dec. 1 ...	12	11.0	9.2	5.3	2.6
1965 Jan. 1 ...	1	12.3	9.5	5.2	2.6
Feb. 1 ...	2	1.5	9.7	5.2	2.7
Mar. 1 ...	3	2.6	9.5	5.3	2.9
Apr. 1 ...	4	3.9	9.1	5.5	3.0
May 1 ...	5	5.2	9.1	5.8	3.1
June 1 ...	6	6.5	9.4	6.0	3.2

TABLE 11 (Cont.)

THE PLANETFINDER

Date	Sun	Venus	Mars	Jupiter	Saturn
July 1 ...	7	7.8	9.8	6.2	3.2
Aug. 1 ...	8	9.0	10.4	6.4	3.2
Sept. 1 ...	9	10.3	11.0	6.6	3.1
Oct. 1 ...	10	11.4	11.7	6.7	3.0
Nov. 1 ...	11	12.5	12.4	6.7	2.9
Dec. 1 ...	12	1.4	1.1	6.7	3.0
1966 Jan. 1 ...	1	2.3	1.9	6.5	3.0
Feb. 1 ...	2	1.8	2.7	6.4	3.1
Mar. 1 ...	3	1.7	3.5	6.4	3.3
Apr. 1 ...	4	2.4	4.2	6.5	3.4
May 1 ...	5	3.5	5.0	6.6	3.5
June 1 ...	6	4.6	5.8	6.8	3.6
July 1 ...	7	5.9	6.5	7.1	3.6
Aug. 1 ...	8	7.1	7.2	7.3	3.6
Sept. 1 ...	9	8.4	7.9	7.6	3.5
Oct. 1 ...	10	9.7	8.5	7.8	3.5
Nov. 1 ...	11	11.0	9.1	7.9	3.4
Dec. 1 ...	12	12.2	9.7	7.9	3.4
1967 Jan. 1 ...	1	1.4	10.2	7.8	3.5
Feb. 1 ...	2	2.7	10.6	7.7	3.5
Mar. 1 ...	3	3.9	10.9	7.6	3.6
Apr. 1 ...	4	5.1	10.8	7.5	3.8
May 1 ...	5	6.4	10.4	7.6	3.9
June 1 ...	6	7.6	10.3	7.8	3.9
July 1 ...	7	8.6	10.5	8.0	4.0
Aug. 1 ...	8	9.3	11.0	8.2	4.0
Sept. 1 ...	9	8.9	11.6	8.4	4.0
Oct. 1 ...	10	8.8	12.3	8.7	3.9
Nov. 1 ...	11	9.5	12.9	8.8	3.9
Dec. 1 ...	12	10.5	1.6	8.9	3.8
1968 Jan. 1 ...	1	11.8	2.4	9.0	3.8
Feb. 1 ...	2	1.0	3.3	8.9	3.9
Mar. 1 ...	3	2.1	4.0	8.6	4.0
Apr. 1 ...	4	3.4	4.8	8.6	4.1
May 1 ...	5	4.5	5.5	8.6	4.2
June 1 ...	6	5.5	6.2	8.7	4.3
July 1 ...	7	7.1	6.9	8.9	4.4
Aug. 1 ...	8	8.4	7.6	9.1	4.5
Sept. 1 ...	9	9.7	8.3	9.3	4.4
Oct. 1 ...	10	10.9	8.9	9.5	4.4
Nov. 1 ...	11	12.2	9.6	9.7	4.3
Dec. 1 ...	12	1.3	10.2	9.9	4.2

TABLE 11 (Cont.)

THE PLANETFINDER

Date	Sun	Venus	Mars	Jupiter	Saturn
1969 Jan. 1 ...	1	2.4	10.8	9.9	4.3
Feb. 1 ...	2	3.6	11.3	10.0	4.3
Mar. 1 ...	3	4.3	11.8	9.9	4.4
Apr. 1 ...	4	4.4	12.2	9.7	4.5
May 1 ...	5	4.0	12.3	9.7	4.6
June 1 ...	6	4.5	12.0	9.6	4.7
July 1 ...	7	5.4	11.8	9.7	4.8
Aug. 1 ...	8	6.6	11.9	9.9	4.9
Sept. 1 ...	9	7.7	12.7	10.0	4.9
Oct. 1 ...	10	9.1	12.9	10.2	4.8
Nov. 1 ...	11	10.4	1.6	10.4	4.8
Dec. 1 ...	12	11.6	2.2	10.5	4.7
1970 Jan. 1 ...	1	12.9	3.1	10.8	4.7
Feb. 1 ...	2	2.1	3.8	10.9	4.7
Mar. 1 ...	3	3.1	4.5	11.0	4.8
Apr. 1 ...	4	4.6	5.3	10.9	4.9
May 1 ...	5	5.9	5.9	10.8	5.0
June 1 ...	6	7.2	6.7	10.7	5.1
July 1 ...	7	8.0	7.6	10.6	5.3
Aug. 1 ...	8	9.4	8.0	10.7	5.4
Sept. 1 ...	9	10.6	8.7	10.8	5.4
Oct. 1 ...	10	11.3	9.8	11.0	5.4
Nov. 1 ...	11	11.5	10.0	11.2	5.3
Dec. 1 ...	12	11.1	10.6	11.4	5.2

Bibliography

General textbooks:

Baker, R. H. *An Introduction to Astronomy.* 6th ed. Princeton: D. Van Nostrand, 1960.
Brief edition of a standard text.

Fath, E. A. *Elements of Astronomy.* 5th ed. New York: McGraw-Hill, 1955.
Well-balanced standard text.

Inglis, S. J. *Planets, Stars, and Galaxies.* New York: John Wiley & Sons, 1961.
Non-mathematical, with emphasis on modern ideas.

Krogdahl, W. S. *The Astronomical Universe.* 2nd ed. New York: Macmillan, 1962.
Very readable critical presentation.

McLaughlin, D. B. *Introduction to Astronomy.* Boston: Houghton Mifflin, 1961.
Complete, authoritative, well-written.

Mehlin, T. G. *Astronomy.* New York: John Wiley & Sons, 1959.
Unorthodox arrangement but fascinating reading.

Skilling, W. T., and Richardson, R. S. *Brief Text in Astronomy.* Rev. ed. New York: Holt, Rinehart and Winston, 1959.
Standard treatment without extraneous material.

Struve, O., Lynds, B., and Pillans, H. *Elementary Astronomy.* New York: Oxford University Press, 1959.
Excellent, but strong emphasis on mathematics and physics.

133

Monographs and less technical references:

Aller, L. H. *Gaseous Nebulae*. New York: John Wiley & Sons, 1956.

Bartky, W. *Highlights of Astronomy*. Chicago: University of Chicago Press, 1961.

Beet, E. A. *The Sky and Its Mysteries*. New York: Dover Publications, 1957.

Bernhard, H. J., Bennett, D. A., and Rice, H. S. *New Handbook of the Heavens*. New York: McGraw-Hill, 1948.

Binnendijk, L. *Properties of Double Stars*. Philadelphia: University of Pennsylvania Press, 1960.

Bok, B. J., and Bok, P. F. *The Milky Way*. 3rd ed. Cambridge: Harvard University Press, 1957.

Gamow, G. *The Creation of the Universe*. Rev. ed. New York: Viking Press, 1961.

Hoyle, F. *Frontiers of Astronomy*. New York: Harper and Row, 1955.

Hubble, E. P. *The Realm of the Nebulae*. New York: Dover Publications, 1958.

Kruse, W., and Dieckvoss, W. *The Stars*. Ann Arbor: University of Michigan Press, 1957.

Lovell, A. C. B. *The Individual and the Universe*. New York: Harper and Row, 1959.

Mayall, N., Mayall, M., and Wyckoff, J. *Sky Observer's Guide*. New York: Golden Press, 1959.

Menzel, D. H. *Our Sun*. Rev. ed. Cambridge: Harvard University Press, 1959.

Nininger, H. H. *Out of the Sky*. New York: Dover Publications, 1959.

Olcott, W. T. *Field Book of the Skies*. Rev. ed. New York: G. P. Putnam's Sons, 1954.

Page, T. *Stars and Galaxies*. Englewood Cliffs: Prentice-Hall, 1962.

Payne-Gaposchkin, C. *The Galactic Novae*. New York: Interscience Publishers, 1957.

———. *Stars in the Making*. Cambridge: Harvard University Press, 1952.

Rey, H. *The Stars.* 2nd ed. Boston: Houghton Mifflin, 1961.

Scientific American (ed). *The New Astronomy.* New York: Simon and Schuster, 1956.

——. *The Universe.* New York: Simon and Schuster, 1957.

Struve, O., and Zebergs, V. *Astronomy of the Twentieth Century.* New York: Macmillan, 1962.

Periodicals:

Popular Astronomy. St. Louis: Sky Map Publications.

Sky and Telescope. Cambridge: Sky Publishing Corporation.

Index

Numbers in **Boldface** indicate photographs or figures.

Chart 1

Year-Round Constellations

Chart II

Seasonal Constellations

On meridian:
(North)
Jan. 1 at 6 pm
Feb. 1   4 pm
Mar. 1   2 pm
Apr. 1   noon
May 1   10 am
Jun. 1   8 am
Jul. 1   6 am
Aug. 1   4 am
Sep. 1   2 am
Oct. 1   midn.
Nov. 1   10 pm
Dec. 1   8 pm

On meridian:
(North)
Jan. 1 at 4 pm
Feb. 1   2 pm
Mar. 1   noon
Apr. 1   10 am
May 1   8 am
Jun. 1   6 am
Jul. 1   4 am
Aug. 1   2 am
Sep. 1   midn.
Oct. 1   10 pm
Nov. 1   8 pm
Dec. 1   6 pm

5 pm
3 pm
1 pm
11 am
9 am
7 am
5 am
3 am
1 am
midn.
10 pm
8 pm
6 pm
3.5
Zenith

4
Zenith

7 pm
5 pm
3 pm
1 pm
11 am
9 am
7 am
5 am
3 am
1 am
midn.
11 pm
9 pm

On meridian:
(North)
Jan. 1 at 8 pm
Feb. 1   6 pm
Mar. 1   4 pm
Apr. 1   2 pm
May 1   noon
Jun. 1   10 am
Jul. 1   8 am
Aug. 1   6 am
Sep. 1   4 am
Oct. 1   2 am
Nov. 1   midn.
Dec. 1   10 pm

On meridian:
(North)
Jan. 1 at 2 pm
Feb. 1   noon
Mar. 1   10 am
Apr. 1   8 am
May 1   6 am
Jun. 1   4 am
Jul. 1   2 am
Aug. 1   midn.
Sep. 1   10 pm
Oct. 1   8 pm
Nov. 1   6 pm
Dec. 1   4 pm

3 pm
1 pm
11 am
9 am
7 am
5 am
3 am
1 am
midn.
10 pm
8 pm
6 pm
2.5
Zenith

3
Zenith

2
Zenith

Delta
CEPHEUS
CASSIOPEIA
PERSEUS
Marfak
Algol
5
Zenith

4.3
Zenith

6
Zenith

On meridian:
(North)
Jan. 1 at 10 pm
Feb. 1   8 pm
Mar. 1   6 pm
Apr. 1   4 pm
May 1   2 pm
Jun. 1   noon
Jul. 1   10 am
Aug. 1   8 am
Sep. 1   6 am
Oct. 1   4 am
Nov. 1   2 am
Dec. 1   midn.

5.5
Zenith

1 pm
11 am
9 am
7 am
5 am
3 am
1 am
11 pm
9 pm
7 pm
5 pm
3 pm
1.5
Zenith

CYGNUS · Deneb
1
CEPHEUS
2

AURIGA
Capella
6.5
Zenith

7
Zenith

On meridian:
(North)
Jan. 1 at midn.
Feb. 1   10 pm
Mar. 1   8 pm
Apr. 1   6 pm
May 1   4 pm
Jun. 1   2 pm
Jul. 1   noon
Aug. 1   10 am
Sep. 1   8 am
Oct. 1   6 am
Nov. 1   4 am
Dec. 1   2 am

11 am
9 am
7 am
5 am
3 am
1 am
11 pm
9 pm
7 pm
5 pm
3 pm
1 pm
noon

On meridian:
(North)
Jan. 1 at noon
Feb. 1   10 am
Mar. 1   8 am
Apr. 1   6 am
May 1   4 am
Jun. 1   2 am
Jul. 1   midn.
Aug. 1   10 pm
Sep. 1   8 pm
Oct. 1   6 pm
Nov. 1   4 pm
Dec. 1   2 pm

1
Zenith

Etamin
DRACO
Polaris
L. DIPPER
Kochab
Thuban
Alpha
G. DIPPER

7.5
Zenith

8
Zenith

On meridian:
(North)
Dec. 1
Nov. 1
Oct. 1
Sep. 1
Aug. 1
Jul. 1
Jun. 1
May 1
Apr. 1
Mar. 1
Feb. 1
Jan. 1 at 2 pm

On meridian:
(North)
Jan. 1 at 10 am
Feb. 1   8 am
Mar. 1   6 am
Apr. 1   4 am
May 1   2 am
Jun. 1   midn.
Jul. 1   10 pm
Aug. 1   8 pm
Sep. 1   6 pm
Oct. 1   4 pm
Nov. 1   2 pm
Dec. 1   noon

12.5
Zenith

Eta
Alcor
Mizar
Beta
8.5
Zenith

12
Zenith

11.5
Zenith

11
Zenith

10.5
Zenith

10
Zenith

9.5
Zenith

9
Zenith

Dec. 1
Nov. 1
Oct. 1
Sep. 1
Aug. 1
Jul. 1
Jun. 1
May 1
Apr. 1
Mar. 1
Feb. 1
Jan. 1 at 4 am

On meridian:
(North)

11 am
9 am
7 am
5 am
3 am
1 am
11 pm
9 pm
7 pm
5 pm
3 pm
noon

9 am
7 am
5 am
3 am
1 am
midn.
10 pm
8 pm
6 pm
4 pm
2 pm

On meridian:
(North)
Jan. 1 at 6 am
Feb. 1   4 am
Mar. 1   2 am
Apr. 1   midn.
May 1   10 pm
Jun. 1   8 pm
Jul. 1   6 pm
Aug. 1   4 pm
Sep. 1   2 pm
Oct. 1   noon
Nov. 1   10 am
Dec. 1   8 am

On meridian:
(North)
Jan. 1 at 4 am
Feb. 1   2 am
Mar. 1   midn.
Apr. 1   10 pm
May 1   8 pm
Jun. 1   6 pm
Jul. 1   4 pm
Aug. 1   2 pm
Sep. 1   noon
Oct. 1   10 am
Nov. 1   8 am
Dec. 1   6 am

CHART II

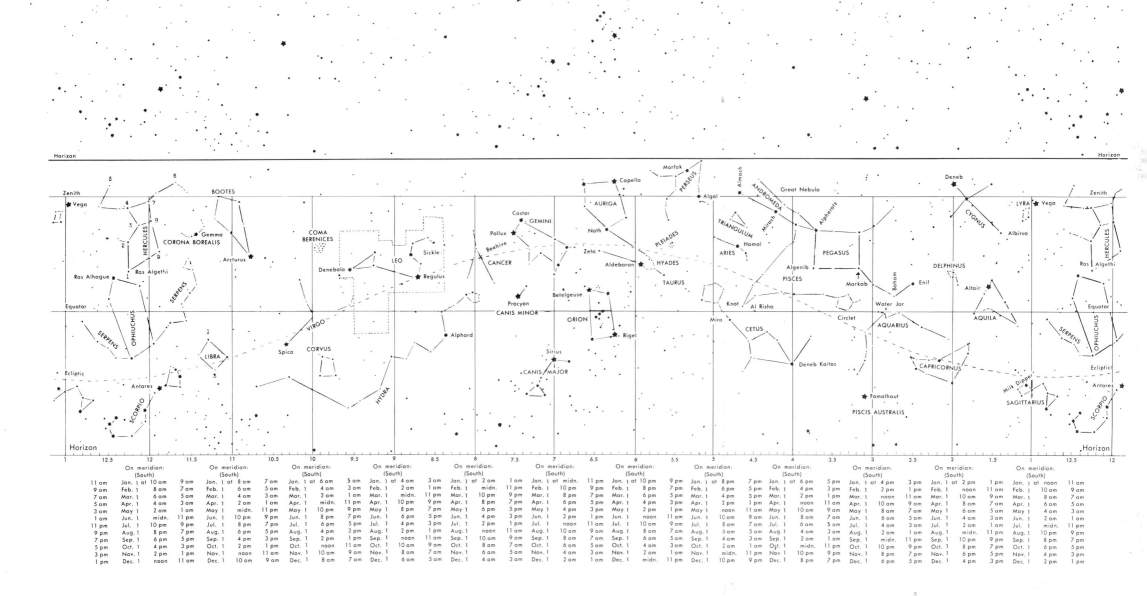